THE BIOLOGY
of the
HETEROPTERA

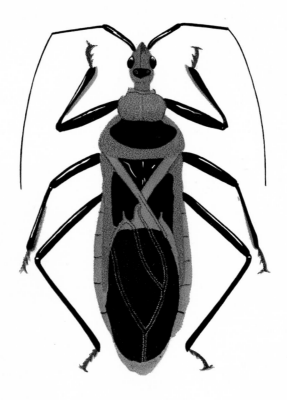

Plynoides elegans Miller 1950. (Reduviidæ-Reduviinæ).

THE BIOLOGY

OF THE

HETEROPTERA

by

N. C. E. MILLER

F.R.E.S., F.E.S.S.A.

Senior Entomologist
Commonwealth Institute of Entomology
London

First published 1956

Printed and bound by
BARNICOTTS LIMITED
at THE WESSEX PRESS
TAUNTON, SOMERSET

CONTENTS

6 4041

LIST OF PLATES

vi

INTRODUCTION

The Hemiptera are divided into two main groups, the Heteroptera and the Homoptera. This division is based on the structure of the mesothoracic or forewings (hemelytra) the basal part of which (corium) is almost entirely coriaceous and the apical part (membrane), membranous.

However, many types of hemelytra are represented, including some in which the corium exhibits considerable diversity in area and structure, for example in the subfamilies Holoptilinæ, and Tribelocephalinæ and in the family Enicocephalidæ.

In the Homoptera the forewings are uniform in structure.

In the classification of the Heteroptera several attempts have been made to find a satisfactory natural arrangement. They have been divided by Dufour into three series, the Geocorisæ (land bugs), Hydrocorisæ (aquatic bugs) and Amphibiocorisæ (bugs living on the surface of the water).

In the first-mentioned group fall all terrestrial bugs and into the second group those living on or in the water. Most of these, however, do leave one area of water to fly to another from time to time.

Aquatic Heteroptera are confined mainly to fresh water, but to quote exceptions, *Halobates* species occur on the sea and the curious *Aepophilus* (Aepophilidæ) lives in rock crevices in the inter-tidal zone of the seashore.

Associated with the Hydrocorisæ are two families of shore bugs, (Gelastocoridæ and Pelogoniidæ), while the largely littoral Saldidæ are probably more correctly associated with the Hydrocorisæ.

Up to the present time, some 25,000 species of Heteroptera are known. While most of them are distributed in the tropics, some families are better represented in the Holarctic Region and some are extremely restricted in range. Fossil remains of Heteroptera have been found in the Carboniferous.

In size the Heteroptera range from about 2 to 100 millimetres in length; among the giants of the insect world are the aquatic genera *Lethocerus* Mayr 1852, *Hydrocyrius* Spinola 1850 and *Belostoma* Latreille 1807, (Belostomatidæ), while the smallest representatives are found in the Dipsocoridæ, Schizopteridæ and Helotrephidæ.

Some species are cosmopolitan having attained their wide distribution in most instances through the agency of man. Among these are *Nezara viridula* Linnæus 1758 (Pentatomidæ), *Liorhyssus hyalinus* (Fabricius) 1794 (Coreidæ), *Nabis capsiformis* Germar 1837 (Nabidæ), *Trigonotylus brevipes* Jakowleff 1880, *Lygus apicalis*

Fieber 1861 (Miridæ) and *Amphibolus venator* Klug 1830 (Reduviidæ). There are also the well-known bed-bug *Cimex lectularius* Linnæus 1758 (Cimicidæ) which is to be found in almost every land, and the aquatic *Halobates micans* Escholtz 1822 (Gerridæ) which is known from several oceans.

Terrestrial species are found on plants, on various parts of which they feed. Some are carnivorous and feed on other Arthropods; others feed on mammalian and avian blood; some species are termitocolous or myrmecophilous.

There are no true cavernicolous Heteroptera. Species recorded from caves have been found usually not very far from the entrance and not often in the more remote parts where it is quite dark. No species has yet been recorded exhibiting characters which indicate that is has become adapted to a life in obscurity. Species feeding on mammalian and avian blood belong to the subfamily Triatominæ. Some of these are eminently important from the medical point of view, since they are vectors of human trypanosomiasis.

The Heteroptera are provided with salivary glands situated mainly in the thorax, but sometimes these glands extend partly into the head or abdomen. In phytophagous species the saliva is injected into the tissues of the host-plant when the bug pierces them with its mouthparts. It acts as an enzyme which breaks down the starch in the sap.

The effect of the saliva on plant tissues is mostly of one type. The area around the site of puncture changes colour fairly rapidly, from brown to black. Following this, the affected part soon wilts and in the event of the damage being extensive the entire plant may perish. When leaves are pierced it is not uncommon for the area surrounding the site of the puncture to dry up and split.

In view of the damage which quite a few Heteroptera are capable of inflicting on plants, it is obvious that they play an important rôle economically. The saliva of predaceous species acts both as an anticoagulin and also lethally; its action on man provokes intense pain.

Glands, variously known as 'scent', 'odoriferous', 'stink' or 'repugnatorial' are present in most Heteroptera both in adults and in the immature stages. Some Heteroptera secrete a glutinous substance through glandular setæ and some, a white wax-like substance which may possibly have some connexion with ecdysis.

A glutinous substance is produced by some species at the time of oviposition. This serves either to fix the ovum to the substratum or possibly to provide protection against hymenopterous parasites. It may also act as a protective covering to check loss of moisture.

Development in the Heteroptera is of the Hemimetabolous (Paurometabolous) type. In this the adult stage is preceded by stages which resemble it to some extent. During the course of development the external changes which take place (apart from increase of size) affect mainly the antennæ, wings and legs. These changes are dealt with in the chapter on Development.

Some difference of opinion exists regarding the use of the term 'larva' to denote the developmental stages between the ovum and the adult. For the apterygota and exopterygota certain authors have adopted the name 'nymph' which they consider to be applicable to all the stages of post-embryonal development. Other authors, however, restrict the designation 'nymph' to the ultimate and penultimate instars in which the wing rudiments become visible.

Berlese has suggested the names 'prosopon' or 'prosopide' for the developmental stages, but on account of the fact, it would seem, that they are not easily pronounced, they have not been widely accepted. In an attempt to settle the matter, Grandi coined a new term 'neanide' which has been found acceptable and has subsequently been used by several authors. I would suggest that all hemipterists should employ it. The term 'nymph' I consider to be singularly inappropriate.

Although the volume of work on the Heteroptera has attained considerable proportions chiefly from the systematic aspect, our knowledge of the biology of the sub-Order is extremely limited. This, I believe, is mainly because attention has been chiefly confined to the collection of specimens and not to recording at the time, facts concerning the habits and habitats of the species concerned.

In this book I have attempted to collate as fully as possible the biological information which is scattered in the voluminous literature. Added to this are also personal observations made in the field in various parts of eastern and central Africa and in Malaysia.

It has not been practicable, obviously, to quote all the literature both on the systematics and biology of the Heteroptera but it is hoped that the references given will provide a basis for further studies.

With regard to the names of families and subfamilies, it is pointed out that they are formed from the oldest group name based on a valid genus. Each family is dealt with separately to facilitate reference and to avoid repetition.

For other papers on the developmental stages of Heteroptera, the *Bulletin of Entomological Research, The Review of Applied Entomology, The Journal of Economic Entomology* and the publications of agricultural organizations in the Commonwealth and Empire should be consulted.

In the preparation of this book I have had valuable and freely-given advice from my colleague, the eminent hemipterist Dr. W. E. China, Keeper of the Department of Entomology, British Museum (Natural History), London. I have also had access to the very extensive collections, card-indices and library of the British Museum. For this very desirable privilege I am greatly indebted to the Trustees.

Finally, I express my sincere thanks to the late Sir Harold Tempany, C.M.G., C.B.E., formerly Director of Agriculture, Straits Settlements and Federated Malay States, and later Agricultural Advisor to the Colonial Office, for his much appreciated support; and to Dr. W. J. Hall, M.C., C.M.G., Director of the Commonwealth Institute of Entomology, London, for permission to carry out the work.

The coloured plate and all the line figures have been prepared by myself, except in those cases in which the authorship is acknowledged. For the photographic plates I have to thank the Photographic Department of the British Museum, (N.H.) London.

References

Amyot and Serville 1843; Berlese 1914; Butler 1923; China 1933, 1943, 1955b; China and Miller 1955; Costa Lima 1940; Distant 1904; Douglas and Scott 1865; Dufour 1833; Ekblom 1926; Evans 1948; Grandi 1951; Hemming 1953; Horvath 1911, 1912; Hungerford 1919; Imms 1934; Jeannel 1919; Kirkaldy 1906; Kalshoven 1950; Kirkaldy 1899; Maxwell-Lefroy 1909; Miller 1931 b, 1934, 1953; Myers 1926; Oshanin 1912; Poisson 1924, 1935, 1951; Readio 1927; Saunders 1892; Southall 1730; Spinola 1837; Thomas 1954; Usinger 1946; Villiers 1952; Weber 1930; Wigglesworth 1939; Reuter 1912.

PART 1

GENERAL ACCOUNT OF THE HETEROPTERA

PART 1

Chapter 1

FAMILY AND SUBFAMILY NAMES OF HETEROPTERA

Family Plataspidæ Dallas 1851, *List. Hem.* **1**, 61.
Syn. Coptosominæ Kirkaldy 1909, *Cat. Hemipt.* **1**, Cimicidæ, 36.
Syn. Coptosomatidæ Reuter 1912, *Öfvers finska VetensSoc.
Förh.* **56**a, No. 6, 45.
Syn. Brachyplatidæ Leston 1952, *Ann. Mag. nat. Hist.* (12) **5**, 512.
Family Cydnidæ Billberg 1820, *Enum. Ins. Mus. Billb.* 10.
Subfamily 1. Corimelæninæ Uhler 1872, *Rep. U.S. geol. Survey*
(1871), **4**, 471.
Syn. Thyreocorinæ Van Duzee 1907, *Bull. Buffalo Soc. nat.
Sci.* **8**, 5, 5.
2. Cydninæ Dallas 1851, *List. Hem.* **1**, 109.
3. Canopinæ Horvath 1919, *Ann. Mus. Nat. Hung.* **17**, 205.
4. Megaridinæ McAtee and Malloch 1928, *Proc. U.S. nat.
Mus.* **72**, 1-21.
Family Pentatomidæ Leach 1815, *Brewster's Edinburgh Encyclopæ-
dia*, **9**, 121.
Subfamily 1. Asopinæ Spinola 1850, *Tav. Sin. Hem.* ex *Mem. Nat.
Fis. Soc. Ital. Sci. Modena* **25**, 1, 69 (1852).
Syn. Amyotinæ Schouteden 1906, *Wytsman Genera Ins.*
50, 2, 2.
Syn. Amyotinæ Leston 1953, *Ent. Gaz.* **4**, 19.
Syn. Arminæ Bergroth 1908, *Mém. Soc. ent. belg.* **15**, 180.
2. Tessaratominæ Stål 1864, *Hem Afr.* **1**, 33.
3. Eumenotinæ Esaki 1922, *Ins.Insc. Mens.* **10**, 196, (under
Aradidæ); 1930 *Ann. Mag. nat. Hist.* (10), **5**, 630,
(under Pentatomidæ).
4. Cyrtocorinæ Distant 1880, *Biol. Centr. Amer.* **1**, 43.
5. Dinidorinæ Stål 1870, *Enum. Hem.* **1**, 79.
Syn. Coridiinæ Schumacher 1924, *Dtsch. ent. Z.* 335.
6. Phyllocephalinæ Dallas 1851, *List. Hem.* **1**, 350.
7. Pentatominæ Stål 1864, *Hem. Afr.* **1**, 32, 76.
Syn. Aeliidæ Douglas and Scott 1865, *Brit. Hem.* 14.
Syn. Sciocoridæ Douglas and Scott 1865, *Brit. Hem.* 13.
Syn. Rhaphigastridæ Douglas and Scott 1865, *Brit. Hem.* 16.
8. Tahitocorinæ Yang 1935, *Ann. mag. Nat. Hist.* (10),
16, 476-482.
9. Scutellerinæ Leach 1815, *Brewster's Edinburgh Encyclopædia*, **9**, 121.

Syn. Odontoscelidæ Douglas and Scott 1865, *Brit. Hem.*13.
Syn. Eurygastridæ Douglas and Scott 1865, *Brit. Hem.* 13.
   10. Podopinæ Dallas 1851, *List. Hem.* 1. 51.(Amyot and
       Serville 1843 *Hém.* XVIII and 65.)
Syn. Graphosomatinæ Jakowleff 1884, *Horæ Soc. ent. ross.*
       18, 204.
   11. Serbaninæ Leston 1953, *Rev. bras. Biol.* **13**, 137.
Family Acanthosomidæ Stål 1864, *Hem. Afr.* **1**, 33, 219. (Leston
       1953 *Ent. Gaz.* **4**, 20).
Family Aphylidæ Bergroth 1906, *Zool. Anz.* **29**, 646 (Aphylinæ).
       Reuter 1912 *Öfvers. Finska VetensSoc. Förh.* **54a**,
       No. 6, 46. (Aphylidæ).
Family Urostylidæ Dallas 1851, *List. Hem.* **1**, 313.
Syn. Urolabidæ Stål 1876, *K. svenska VeternskAkad. Hand.* **14**,
       4, 115.
Family Phlœidæ Dallas, 1851, *List. Hem.* **1**, 149.
Family Coreidæ Leach 1815, *Brewster's Edinburgh Encyclopædia* **9**,121.
Subfamily 1. Merocorinæ Stål 1870, *Enum. Hem.* **1**, 125.
        2. Rhopalinæ Amyot and Serville 1843, *Hém.* XXXVI
           and 243.
Syn. Corizidæ Douglas and Scott 1865, *Brit. Hem.* 17.
Syn. Chorosomidæ Douglas and Scott 1865, *Brit. Hem.*17.
Syn. Corizinæ Mayr 1866, Reise Freg. Novara, Zool. **2**,
       Hemip. 121.
        3. Alydinæ Dallas 1852, *List. Hem.* **2**, 467. (Amyot and
           Serville 1843, *Hém.* XXXIV and 221).
Syn. Stenocephalidæ Douglas and Scott 1865, *Brit.Hem.*18.
Syn. Coriscidæ Stichel 1925, *Illus. Bestimmungstabellen
       Deutsch. Wanz.* 45.
        4. Coreinæ Stål 1867, *Öfvers. VetenskAkad. Förh.
           Stockh.* 24, 535.
        5. Pseudophlœinæ Stål 1867, *Öfvers. Vetensk Akad.
           Förh. Stockh.* **24**, 535.
Syn. Arenocorinæ Bergroth 1913, *Mém. Soc. ent. Belg.* **32**,
       155.
        6. Agriopocorinæ Miller 1953, *Proc. Linn. Soc. N.S.W.*
           78, 233.
Family Hyocephalidæ Bergroth 1906, *Zool. Anz.* **29**, 649.
Family Lygæidæ Schilling 1829, *Beitr. z. Ent.* **1**, 37.
Syn. Myodochidæ Kirkaldy 1899, *Entomologist* **32**, 220.
Subfamily 1. Rhyparochrominæ Stål 1862, *Öfvers. VetenskAkad.
           Förh. Stockh.* **19**, 210.
Syn. Aphaninæ Letheirry and Severin 1894, *Cat. Gen. Hem,*
       2, 188.

2. Geocorinæ Stål 1862, *Öfvers. VetenskAkad Förh.*, *Stockh.* **19**, 212.
3. Blissinæ Stål 1862, *Öfvers. VetenskAkadFörh.Stockh.* **19**, 210.
4. Cyminæ Stål 1862, *Öfvers. VetenskAkad. Förh. Stockh.* **19**, 211.
5. Lygæinæ Stål 1862, *Öfvers. VetenskAkad. Förh. Stockh.* **19**, 210.
Syn. Astacopinæ Kirkaldy 1907, *Canad. Ent.* **39**, 244.
6. Oxycareninæ Stål 1862, *Öfvers. VetenskAkad. Förh. Stockh.* **19**, 212.
7. Pamphantinæ Barber and Bruner 1933, *J. N.Y. ent. Soc.* **41**, 532.
8. Malcinæ Stål 1865, *Hem. Afr.* **2**, 121.
9. Lipostemmatinæ Berg. 1879, *Hem. Argent.* 288.
10. Bledionotinæ Reuter 1878, *Ann. Soc. ent. Fr.* 144.
11. Henestarinæ Douglas and Scott 1865, *Brit. Hem.* 22. (Henestaridæ).
12. Pachygronthinæ Stål 1765, *Hem. Afr.* **2**, 121, 145.
13. Heterogastrinæ Stål 1872, *Öfvers. VetenskAkad. Förh., Stockh.* **29**, 40, 62.
Syn. Phygadicidæ Douglas and Scott 1865, *Brit. Hem.* 21.
Syn. Chauliopinæ Breddin 1907, *Dtsch. ent. Z.* 40.
14. Artheneinæ Stål 1872, *Öfvers. VetenskAkad. Förh. Stockh.* **29**, 38, 47.

Family Pyrrhocoridæ Dohrn 1859, *Cat. Hem.* 36 (Amyot and Serville 1843, *Hém.* XXXVIII and 265).
Syn. Astemmatidæ Spinola 1850, *Tav. Sin. Hem.* ex *Mem. Mat. Fis. Soc. Ital. Sci. Modena*, **25**, 79 (1852).

Family Largidæ Dohrn 1859, *Cat. Hem.* 36. (Amyot and Serville 1843 *Hém.* XXXVIII, 273).
Syn. Euryopthalminæ Van Duzee 1916, Check List *Hem. Amer. N. of Mexico* 24.

Family Piesmidæ Spinola 1850, *Tav. Sin. Hem.* ex *Mem. Mat. Fis. Soc. Ital. Sci. Modena.* **25**, 84. (1852).
Syn. Zosmenidæ Dohrn 1859, *Cat. Hem.* 41.
Syn. Zosmeridæ Douglas and Scott 1865, *Brit. Hem.* 237. (Zosmeridæ in error, page 22).

Family Thaumastocoridæ Kirkaldy 1908, *Proc. Linn. Soc. N.S.W.* **32**, 789. (Corrigenda).
Syn. Thaumastotheriinæ *loc. cit.* 777.

Family Berytidæ Fieber 1951, *Genera Hydroc.* 9.
Syn. Neididæ Kirkaldy 1902, *J. Bombay nat. Hist. Soc.* **14**, 302.
Subfamily 1. Berytinæ Puton 1886 *Cat. Hem. Palæarct.* edn. 3, 19.

2. Metacanthinæ Douglas and Scott 1865, *Brit. Hem.* 99 and 145.

Family Colobathristidæ Stål 1865, *Hem. Afr.* **2**, 121.

Family Aradidæ Amyot and Serville 1843, *Hém.* 306.

Family Meziridæ Oshanin 1908, *Verz. Paläark. Hem.* 478.

Syn. Brachyrhynchidæ Amyot and Serville 1843, *Hém.* XLI and 303. (Based on a homonym and therefore unusable.)

Syn. Dysodiidæ Reuter 1912, *Öfvers. finska VetenskSoc. Förh.*, **33**, 49 and 57.

Subfamily 1. Isoderminæ Stål 1872 *Svensk. Vet-Ak. Handl.* 10, 4.

2. Mezirinæ Oshanin 1908, *Verz. Paläark. Hem.* 478.

Syn. Chelonocorinæ Miller 1938, *Ann. Mag. nat. Hist.* (11) **1**, 498-510.

Family Aneuridæ Douglas and Scott 1865, *Brit. Hem.* 26, 267.

Family Termitaphididæ Myers 1924, *Psyche, Camb., Mass.*, **31**, 267.

Syn. Termitocoridæ Silvestri 1911, *Boll. Lab. Zool. Portici* **5**, 231-236.

Family Joppeicidæ Reuter 1910, *Acta Soc. Sci. fenn.*, **37**, 75.

Family Tingidæ Laporte 1832, *Essai Classif. Syst. Hém.* 47.

Syn. Tingidinæ Amyot and Serville 1843, *Hém.* II and 295.

Subfamily 1. Tinginæ Douglas and Scott 1865, *Brit. Hem.* 24.

2. Cantacaderinæ Stål 1873, *Enum. Hem.* **3**, 116.

3. Agramminæ Douglas and Scott 1865, *Brit. Hem.* 24 and 242. (Agrammidæ).

Syn. Serenthiinæ Stål 1873, *Enum. Hem.* **3**, 116.

Family Enicocephalidæ Stål 1860, *Rio Jan. Hem.* **1**, 81.

Syn. Henicocephalidæ Stål 1865, *Hem. Afr.* **3**, 165.

Family Phymatidæ Laporte 1832 *Essai Classif. Syst. Hém.* 14.

Syn. Macrocephalidæ Kirkaldy 1899, *Entomologist* **32**, 221.

Subfamily 1. Macrocephalinæ Dohrn 1859, *Cat. Hem.* 141. (Amyot and Serville 1843, *Hém.* XXXIX and 291).

2. Phymatinæ Dohrn 1859, *Cat. Hem.* 141. (Amyot and Serville 1843, *Hém.* XXXIX and 291).

3. Carcinocorinæ Handlirsch 1897, *Ann. K.K. Nat. Hofmus. Wien* **12**, 142.

Family Elasmodemidæ Letheirry and Severin 1896, *Cat.Gen.Hém.*2,49.

Syn. Elasmocorinæ Usinger 1943, *Ann. ent. Soc. Amer.* **36**, 612.

Family Reduviidæ Latreille 1807, *Gen. Crust. Ins.* **3**, 126.

Subfamily 1. Holoptilinæ Stål 1859, *Berl. ent. Z.* 328.

2. Emesinæ Spinola 1850, *Tav. Sin. Hem.* ex *Mem. Mat. Fis. Soc. Ital. Sci. Modena* **25**, 45 (1852). (Amyot and Serville 1843, *Hém.* XLVIII and 393).

Syn. Ploiariinæ Costa 1852, *Cimic. Reg. Neap. Cent.* **4**, 66. (Kirkaldy 1902, *Faun. Hawaiien.* **3**, 151).

3. Visayanocorinæ Miller 1952, *Eos Madr.* **28**, 88-89.
4. Saicinæ Stål 1859, *Berl. ent. Z.* **3**, 328.
5. Bactrodinæ Stål 1865, *Hem. Afr.* **3**, 45.
6. Tribelocephalinæ Stål 1865, *Hem. Afr.* **3**, 44.
7. Stenopodinæ Stål 1859, *Berl. ent. Z.* **3**, 328. (Amyot and Serville 1843, *Hém.* XLVIII and 386).
8. Salyavatinæ Stål 1859, *Berl. ent. Z.* **3**, 328. (Amyot and Serville 1843, *Hém.* XLVIII and 349),
9. Manangocorinæ Miller 1954, *Idea* **10**, 2.
10. Sphæridopinæ 1940, Costa Lima Ins. Brasil 206.
11. Physoderinæ Miller 1954, *Tijdschr. Ent.* **97**, 82.
12. Chryxinæ Champion 1898, *Biol. cent.-amer.* **2**, 180.
13. Vesciinæ Fracker and Bruner 1924, *Ann. ent. Soc. Amer.* **17**, 165.
Syn. Chopardititæ Villiers 1944, *Bull. Soc. ent. Fr.* **49**, 79.
14. Reduviinæ Spinola 1850, *Tav. Sin. Hem.* ex *Mem. Mat. Fis. Soc. Ital. Sci. Modena*, **25**, 145 (1852).
Syn. Acanthaspidæ Stål 1872, *Öfvers. VetenskAkad. Förh., Stockh.* **19**, 64.
15. Eupheninæ Miller 1955, *Ann. Mag. Nat. Hist.* (12) 8, 449-452.
16. Cetherinæ Jeannel 1919, *Voy. Alluaud Jeann. Afr. or.* 1911-1912, 178.
17. Triatominæ Jeannel 1919, *Voy. Alluaud Jeann. Afr. or.* 176-7.
18. Piratinæ Stål 1859, *Berl. ent. Z.* **3**, 328.
19. Phimophorinæ Handlirsch 1897, *Verh. zool-bot. Ges. Wien.* 408.
20. Pachynominæ Stål 1873, *Enum. Hem.* **3**, 107. (transferred from Nabidæ).
21. Hammacerinæ Stål 1859, *Berl. ent. Z.* 328.
Syn. Hammatoceridæ Stål, *Stettin ent. Ztg.* **23**, 455.
Syn. Microtominæ Schumacher 1924, *Dtsch. ent. Z.* 336.
22. Ectrichodiinæ Spinola 1850, *Tav. Sin. Hem.* ex *Mem. Mat. Fis. Soc. Ital. Sci. Modena* **25**, 44-45 (1852).
23. Perissorhynchinæ Miller 1952, *Eos Madr.* **28**, 87.
24. Rhaphidosominæ Jeannel 1919, *Voy. Alluaud Jeann. Afr. or.* 263.
25. Harpactorinæ Spinola 1850, *Tav. Sin. Hem.* ex *Mem. Mat. Fis. Soc. Ital. Sci. Modena* **25**, 45 (1852). (Amyot and Serville 1843, *Hém.* XLV and 355).
Syn. Reduviinæ Stål 1859, *Öfvers. VetenskAkad. Förh. Stockh.* **16**, 195.
26. Apiomerinæ Stål, *Berl. ent. Z.* **3**, 328. (Amyot and

Serville 1843, *Hém.* XLIV and 350).

27. Ectinoderinæ Stål 1866, *Öfvers. VetenskAkad Förh. Stockh.* 245.

28. Phonolibinæ Miller 1952, *Eos. Madr.* **28,** 86.

29. Tegeinæ Villiers 1948, *Hém. Réduv. Afr. noire* 171.

Family Velocipedidæ Bergroth 1891, *Wien ent. Ztg.* **10,** 265.

Family Nabidæ Costa 1852, *Cimic. Neap. Cent.* **3,** 66.

Subfamily 1. Nabinæ Reuter 1890, *Rev. Ent., Cæn.,* **9,** 293.

Syn. Reduviolinæ Reuter and Poppius 1909, (*nec* Reuter 1890) *Acta Soc. Sci. fenn.* **37,** 3.

Syn. Coriscina Stål 1873, *Enum. Hem.* **3,** 106.

2. Prostemminæ Reuter 1890, *Rev. Ent., Cæn,* **9,** 289.

Syn. Nabinæ Reuter and Poppius 1909, *Acta Soc. Sci. fenn.* **37,** 3.

3. Arachnocorinæ Reuter 1890, *Rev. Ent., Cæn,* **9,** 292.

4. Gorpinæ Reuter 1909, *Ann. Soc. ent. belg.* **53,** 423.

5. Carthasinæ Blatchley 1926, *Het. E. North America* 538-9.

Family Polyctenidæ Westwood 1874, *Thesaur. Ent.* 197.

Family Cimicidæ Latreille (as Cimicides) 1804, *Hist. Nat. Crust. Ins.* **12,** 235; Leach 1815 *Brewster's Edinburgh Encyclopædia,* **9,** 122.

Syn. Acanthiadæ Fieber 1860, *Europ. Hem.* 37 and 135.

Syn. Acanthiidæ Douglas and Scott 1865, *Brit. Hem.* (nec. Leach) 37.

Syn. Cacodmidæ Kirkaldy 1899, *Bull. Lpool. Mus.* **2,** 45.

Syn. Clinocoridæ Kirkaldy 1906, *Trans. Amer. ent. Soc.* **32,** 147.

Subfamily 1. Cimicinæ Van Duzee 1916, *Check List Hem. America N. of Mexico* 33.

2. Hæmatosiphoninæ Jordan and Rothschild 1912, *Novit. zool.* **19,** 352.

3. Cacodminæ Kirkaldy 1899, *Bull. Lpool. Mus.* **2,** 45.

4. Primicimicinæ Usinger and Ferris (in press).

Family Anthocoridæ Fieber 1851, *Genera Hydroc.* 9. (Amyot and Serville 1843, *Hém.* XXXVII and 262 (Anthocorides).

Subfamily 1. Lyctocorinæ Reuter 1884, *Monog. Anthoc. Acta Soc. Sci. fenn.* **14,** (1885), 558.

2. Anthocorinæ Reuter 1884, *Monog. Anthoc. Acta Soc. Sci. fenn.* **14** (1885), 558.

3. Dufouriellinæ Van Duzee *Check List Hem. America N. of Mexico,* 35.

Syn. Xylocorinæ Reuter 1884, *Monog. Anthoc. Acta Soc.*

Sci. fenn. **14** (1885), 558.

Family Microphysidæ Dohrn 1859, *Cat. Hem.* 36.

Subfamily 1. Microphysinæ China 1953, *Ann. Mag. nat. Hist.* (12), **6,** 73.

2. Plokiophilinæ China 1953, *Ann. Mag. nat. Hist.* (12), **6,** 73.

Family Miridæ Hahn 1831, *Wanz. Ins.* **1,** 234.

Syn. Capsidæ Burmeister 1835, *Handb. Ent. Jena* 2, 263.

Syn. Phytocoridæ Fieber 1858, *Wien ent. Monatschr.* **2,** 289.

Subfamily 1. Mirinæ Reuter 1910, *Acta Soc. Sci. fenn.* **27,** 109 and 128.

Syn. Capsides Amyot and Serville 1843, *Hém.* XXXIX and 278.

Syn. Dichroscytidæ Douglas and Scott 1865, *Brit. Hem.* 34.

Syn. Lopidæ Douglas and Scott 1865, *Brit. Hem.* 34.

Syn. Lygidæ Douglas and Scott 1865, *Brit. Hem.* 33.

Syn. Pithanidæ Douglas and Scott 1865, *Brit. Hem.* 28.

2. Orthotylinæ Van Duzee 1916, *Check List Hem. America N. of Mexico* 203.

Syn. Heterotominæ Reuter 1910 *Acta Soc. Sci. fenn.* **37,** 114.

Syn. Cyllecorinæ Oshanin 1912, *Kat. Paläark. Hem.* 72.

Syn. Stiphrosomidæ Douglas and Scott 1865, *Brit. Hem.* 35.

Syn. Camaronotidæ Douglas and Scott 1865, *Brit. Hem.* 30.

Syn. Globicepidæ Douglas and Scott 1865, *Brit. Hem.* 31.

Syn. Litosomidæ Douglas and Scott 1865, *Brit. Hem.* 30.

Syn. Halticocoridæ Douglas and Scott 1865, *Brit. Hem.* 35.

3. Phylinæ Douglas and Scott 1865, *Brit. Hem.* 30 (Phylidæ) Tribe Phylini (Douglas and Scott) Carvalho 1952 *An. Acad. Brasil. Cien.* **24,** 41.

Syn. Psallidæ Douglas and Scott 1865, *Brit. Hem.* 32.

Syn. Oncotylidæ Douglas and Scott 1865 *Brit. Hem.* 32.

Syn. Harpoceridæ Douglas and Scott 1865 *Brit. Hem.* 33.

Syn. Plagiognathinæ Oshanin 1912, *Kat. Paläark. Hem.* 77.

Tribe Hallodapini (Van Duzee), Carvalho 1952, *An. Acad. Brasil. Cien.* **24,** 41.

Syn. Eroticoridæ Douglas and Scott 1865, *Brit. Hem.* 471. (Myrmicocoridæ Douglas and Scott 1865, *Brit. Hem.* 34, based on *Myrmicocoris* Douglas and Scott (not *Myrmecoris* Gorski) = (Hallodapus Fieber).)

Tribe Dicyphini (Reuter) Carvalho 1952, *An. Acad. Brasil. Cien.* **24,** 41.

Syn. Dicyphinæ Oshanin *Kat. Paläark. Hem.* 70.

Syn. Idolocoridæ Douglas and Scott 1865, *Brit. Hem.* 31.

Syn. Macrolophinæ Kirkaldy 1906, *Canad. Ent.* **38**, 371; Reuter *Acta Soc. Sci. fenn.* **37**, 118.

Subfamily 4. Bryocorinæ Douglas and Scott 1865, *Brit. Hem.* 28 and 276.

5. Deræocorinæ Douglas and Scott 1865, *Brit. Hem.* 29.

Syn. Termatophylidæ Reuter 1888, *Wien. ent. Ztg.* **3**, 218.

Syn. Cliv_neminæ Reuter 1875, *Caps. Bor. Amer.* 62.

Syn. Hyaliodinæ Knight 1943, *Ent. News,* **54** (5), 19.

6. Cylapinæ Kirkaldy 1903 *Wien ent. Ztg.* **22**, 13.

Syn. Bothynotinæ Reuter 1910 *Acta Soc. Sci. fenn.* **27**, 155.

Syn. Teratodellaria Reuter 1875, *Bih. svensk. Vetensk Akad. Handl.* **3**, 5.

Syn. Fulviaria Uhler 1886, *Check List* 19.

Syn. Valdusaria Distant 1883, *Biol. cent-amer.* **1**, 242.

Family Isometopidæ Fieber 1860, *Wien ent. Monat.* **4**, 259.

Family Dipsocoridæ Dohrn 1859, *Cat. Hem.* 36.

Syn. Cryptostemmatidæ McAtee and Malloch 1925, *Proc. U.S. nat. Mus.* **47**, 1.

Syn. Ceratocombidæ Fieber 1861, *Europ. Hem.* **25**, 39 and 142.

Family Schizopteridæ Reuter 1891, *Acta Soc. Sci. fenn.* **19**, 3.

Family Hydrometridæ Billberg 1820, *Enum. Ins. Mus. Billb.* 67.

Syn. Limnobatidæ Douglas and Scott 1865, *Brit. Hem.* 43.

Subfamily 1. Hydrometrinæ Esaki 1927, *Entomologist* **60**, 4.

2. Limnobatodinæ Esaki 1927, *Entomologist* **60**, 4.

3. Heterocleptinæ Villiers 1948, *Réduv. Afr. noire* 174.

Syn. Hydrobatodinæ China and Usinger 1949, *Rev. Zool. Bot. afr.* **41**, 318.

Family Gerridæ Leach 1815, *Brewster's Edinburgh Encyclopædia* **9**, 123. (Amyot and Serville 1843 *Hém.* L. and 318.)

Syn. Hydrometridæ Douglas and Scott 1865, *Brit. Hem.* 41.

Subfamily 1. Gerrinæ Bianchi 1896, *Ann. Mus. Zool. Acad. St. Pétersb.* 69.

2. Halobatinæ Bianchi 1896, *Ann. Mus. Zool. Acad. St. Pétersb.* 69.

3. Hermatobatinæ Coutière and Martin 1901, *C.R. Soc. Biol., Paris* **132**, 1066-68.

4. Rhagadotarsinæ Lundblad 1933, *Arch. Hydrobiol. (Plankt)* 411.

5. Ptilomerinæ Esaki 1927, *Eos Madr.* **2**, 252.

Family Veliidæ Dohrn 1859, *Cat. Hem.* 53. (Amyot and Serville 1843, *Hém.* L. and 418).

Subfamily 1. Macroveliinæ Makinstry 1942, *Pan. Pacif. Ent.* **18**, 91.

2. Perittopinæ China and Usinger 1949 *Ann. Mag. nat. Hist.* (12) **2**, 350.

3. Rhagoveliinæ China and Usinger 1949, *Ann. Mag. nat. Hist.* (12), **2**, 351.
4. Hebroveliinæ Lundblad 1939, *Ent. Tidsk.* **60**, 23.
5. Microveliinæ China and Usinger 1949, *Ann. Mag. nat. Hist.* (12), **2**, 351.
6. Veliinæ China and Usinger 1939, *Ann. Mag. nat. Hist.* (12), **2**, 353.
7. Haloveliinæ Esaki 1930, *J. F.M.S. Mus.* **16**, 22. (as Gerrid).

Family Mesoveliidæ Douglas and Scott 1867, *Ent. mon. Mag.* **4**, 3.
Family Hebridæ Fieber 1851, *Genera Hydroc.* 9. (Amyot and Serville 1843, *Hém.* XL and 293).
Syn. Næogeidæ Kirkaldy 1902, *Fauna Hawaii.* 168.
Family Leotichiidæ China 1953, *Ann. Mag. nat. Hist.* (10), **12**, 185.
Family Leptopodidæ Costa 1838, *Cimic. Reg. Neap. Cent.* **1**, *Atti real. Ist. Incorrag alle Sci. Nat. Nap.* **7**, 151 (1847).
Family Saldidæ Costa 1852, *Cimic. Reg. Neap. cent.* **3**, 66 (Amyot and Serville 1843, *Hém.* XLIX).
Syn. Acanthiidæ Leach 1815, *Brewster's Edinburgh Encyclopædia* **9**, 123.
Family Aepophilidæ Puton 1879, *Syn. Hém. Het. France*, **2**, 145.
Family Notonectidæ Leach 1815, *Brewster's Edinburgh Encyclopædia*, **9**, 124.
Subfamily 1. Anisopinæ Hutchinson 1929, *Ann. S.Afr. Mus.*, **25**, 362.
         2. Notonectinæ Fieber 1860, *Eur. Hem.* 22, 31 and 100.
Family Pleidæ Fieber 1851, *Genera Hydroc.* 27.
Family Helotrephidæ Esaki and China 1927, *Trans. R. ent. Soc. Lond.* 280.
Subfamily 1. Neotrephinæ China 1940, *Ann. Mag. nat. Hist.* (11), **5**, 123.
         2. Idiocorinæ Esaki and China 1927, *Trans. R. ent. Soc. Lond.* 280.
         3. Helotrephinæ Esaki and China 1927, *Trans. R. ent. Soc. Lond.* 280.
Family Corixidæ Leach 1815, *Brewster's Edinburgh Encyclopædia*, **9**, 124.
Subfamily 1. Micronectinæ Jaczewski 1924, *Ann. Mus. zool. polon.* **3**, 3.
Syn. Sigaridæ Douglas and Scott 1865, *Brit. Hem.* 50.
         2. Diaprepocorinæ Lundblad 1928, *Entom. Tidsk.* **1**, 9.
         3. Corixinæ Douglas and Scott 1865, *Brit. Hem.* 50.
         4. Stenocorixinæ Hungerford 1948, *Kans. Univ. Sci. Bull.* **32**, 43.

5. Cymatiinæ Walton 1940, *Trans. Conn. Acad. Arts Sci.* **33**, 344.

6. Heterocorixinæ Hungerford 1948, *Kans. Univ. Sci. Bull.* **32**, 43.

Family Nepidæ Latreille 1802, *Hist. Nat. Crust. Ins.* **3**, 252.

Subfamily 1. Nepinæ Douglas and Scott 1865, *Brit. Hem.* 583.

2. Ranatrinæ Douglas and Scott 1865, *Brit. Hem.* 581.

Family Belostomatidæ Leach 1815, *Brewster's Edinburgh Encyclopædia*, **9**, 123.

Family Naucoridæ Fallen 1814, *Spec. Nov. Disp. Meth.* 3 and 15.

Subfamily 1. Naucorinæ Stål 1876, *Enum. Hem.* **5**, 142.

2. Limnocorinæ Stål 1876, *Enum. Hem.* **5**, 142.

3. Laccocorinæ Stål 1876, *Enum. Hem.* **5**, 142.

4. Cryphocricinæ Montandon 1897, *Verh. zool-bot. Ges. Wien*, **47**, 6.

5. Ambrysinæ Usinger 1941, *Ann. ent. Soc. Amer.* **34**, 911.

6. Cheirochelinæ Montandon 1897, *Ann. Mus. Stor. nat. Genova*, **37**, 367.

7. Potamocorinæ Usinger 1941, *Ann. ent. Soc. Amer.*, **34**, 8 and 9.

8. Aphelocheirinæ Douglas and Scott 1865, *Brit. Hem.* 44.

Family Gelastocoridæ Kirkaldy 1897, *Entomologist* 30, 258.

Syn. Galgulidæ Billberg 1820, *Erum. Ins. Mus. Billb.* 66.

Syn. Nerthridæ Kirkaldy 1906, *Trans. Amer. ent. Soc.* 32, 149.

Subfamily 1. Galgulinæ Billberg 1820, *Enum. Ins. Mus. Billb.* 66.

Syn. Gelastocorinæ Champion 1901, *Biol. Centr. Amer. Het.* **2**, 437.

2. Mononyxinæ Fieber 1851, *Genera Hydroc.* 9 and 12.

Syn. Nerthrinæ Kirkaldy 1906, *Trans. Amer. ent. Soc.* 32, 149.

Family Pelogoniidæ Leach 1815, *Brewster's Edinburgh Encyclopædia*, **9**, 123.

Syn. Ochteridæ Kirkaldy 1906, *Trans. Amer. ent. Soc.* 32, 149.

Chapter 2

DEVELOPMENT

A great diversity of form is exhibited by the ova of the Heteroptera and, so far as our knowledge goes, each group of genera in a subfamily would appear to have a characteristic ovum. It is not correct to say that ova are of a definite type in each subfamily.

The principal constituent of an ovum is the shell or chorion which is formed by a cuticular secretion of the epithelial cells in the oviduct. Generally it is made up of two layers of different thickness and structure and the external surface may be smooth and shining, shagreened or sculptured in one manner or another.

Some Heteropterous ova, notably those of certain Pentatomidæ, have a series of short, hollow appendages, usually somewhat wider at the apex, situated on the upper margin of the chorion. Ova bearing similar appendages are produced by certain Coreidæ, Urostylidæ, Reduviidæ (Emesinæ) and Miridæ.

When these appendages were first noticed and subsequently more closely examined, the conclusion arrived at was that it was through them that the sperm entered the ovum.

This was the opinion of Leuckart who advanced it in a treatise on the eggs of insects, but, about sixty years later, Gross disputed it and suggested that these chorionic processes (Chorion-Anhänge) were for the purpose of ventilating the interior of the ovum.

At the present time this seems to be the opinion generally accepted but, it must be noted that although all ova require air, there are very many, in fact the majority that are not provided with these processes. Aeration in such cases is effected through pores in the operculum or through the chorion itself.

Certain species secrete a glutinous substance which envelops each ovum at the time of deposition, therefore air can penetrate only through the pores in the operculum which is commonly a circular, concavo-convex plate and occasionally has a very complicated structure. (cf. *Rhinocoris* spp. Reduviidæ).

Many methods of oviposition are met with in the Heteroptera; some species deposit their ova in groups, others singly, either with or without a small quantity of glutinous substance to fix them to the substratum.

Then there are those species which insert their ova into the soil or into the softer parts of plants. Aquatic species immerse their ova and attach them to plants or to stones. Exceptionally the dorsum of the male of the same species is selected by the female. (cf. certain Belostomatidæ).

13

The position of the ovum in relation to the substratum varies, some ova being deposited with the longer axis vertical, others at an angle or horizontal. Some ova that have the horizontal position have a short pedicel which raises them above the surface of the object on which they are deposited.

The construction of an ootheca such as is found in the Blattidæ or Mantidæ (Orthoptera), is not met with. The nearest approach to that type of oviposition is that of certain Harpactorinæ (Reduviidæ), namely species of *Sycanus* Amyot and Serville 1843, in which the ova, after deposition in a vertical position, in groups, are covered by the female with a glutinous substance which envelops all of them with the exception of much of the differentiated portion of the chorion. In *Panthous* Stål 1863, of the same subfamily, the ova are completely covered. It should be pointed out that in both cases the glutinous substance does not harden.

In the chapters in which the families are dealt with individually, the various methods of oviposition are described more fully.

At the time of eclosion the chorion may be split in various directions by the embryo, but if there is an operculum, this alone is removed.

To assist the embryo to remove the operculum an egg-burster (Eisprenger), a highly sclerotized portion of the embryonic cuticle, present in the Pentatomidæ, Coreidæ and possibly in other families, is employed. The egg-burster has various shapes. Fig. 1

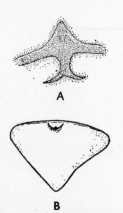

A

B

Fig. 1. EGG BURSTERS

A. *Embolosterna taurus* Westwood 1837. (Pentatomidæ-Tessaratominæ).
B. *Physomerus parvulus* Dallas 1851. (Coreidæ-Coreinæ).

In the Pentatomidæ it is commonly anchor-shaped or has the form of a T with a short, conical spur at one or both ends of the 'shaft' portion; or it may be an elongate rod with the middle portion thickened.

In the case of the Pentatomidæ, when eclosion is taking place, one or both spurs engage with the rim of the chorion and of the operculum, so that the latter, when raised may not close again when embryo retracts prior to distending itself once more to lift the operculum higher.

The initial split in the chorion is made by the egg-burster of Coreidæ, but after that it does not render further assistance to the embryo disengaging itself from the chorion.

An analogous organ is present in the

Reduviidæ but its purpose is not exactly the same as in the instances just mentioned, that is to say, to pierce the chorion.

It consists of two groups of very small denticles, more strongly sclerotized parts of the embryonic cuticle which, it would seem, engage with the lower surface of the operculum to facilitate its removal. When the operculum is sufficiently raised, or when the gap between it and the chorion has been adequately widened, the embryo, by even greater distension of its body causes the enveloping cuticle to split and is able then to free itself completely. The operculum and the cuticle often remain on the empty chorion.

So far as observations go, newly hatched neanides remain on or close by the empty ova until they moult for the first time. During that period they feed very little or not at all.

Neanides from ova deposited in groups are often gregarious during the first instar, but disperse after the first moult. In some species of Coreidæ, Aradidæ and Pyrrhocoridæ which often oviposit on isolated plants or in a restricted area, the neanides remain together until they reach the adult stage.

Examples of this gregarious habit may be seen in the Coreids, *Petascelis remipes* Signoret 1847, an Ethiopian species, *Physomerus grossipes* (Fabricius) 1794, an abundant species in Malaysia, the Pyrrhocorids *Dysdercus* spp. Amyot and Serville 1843, represented in the Ethiopian and Oriental Regions, and it is interesting to note that the adults also remain with the neanides. It is possible, therefore, to see all stages of these bugs together at one time.

At the time of ecdysis the neanide attaches itself as firmly as possible to the substratum with its tarsal claws and frequently takes up a position in which it hangs head downwards.

By distending itself with air it causes the cuticle to split along the so-called ecdysial line, a narrow, feebly sclerotized part located between the eyes, extending along the postocular portion of the head and along the nota to the first abdominal segment.

By successive convulsive movements the neanide then extricates the antennae, head, and anterior legs and with these legs obtains a hold on some object close by. It then drags out the remaining legs and the body. Sometimes it relies on gravity to assist it to quit the exuviæ.

After ecdysis, a neanide remains quiescent for some time until the integument has hardened sufficiently. The period elapsing before the integument is hard and firm may cover several days.

The development of the pigment as a rule takes less time, but it may be less rapid in those species that live where very little light penetrates.

From the time of eclosion to maturity, neanides usually pass through five or six instars and at each moult some modification, slight in the early instars but greater in succeeding ones, takes place in the external appearance. This modification concerns mainly the hemelytra and the metathoracic wings, the rudiments of which are plainly visible generally in the fourth and fifth instars, but less so in the third instar.

Other modifications comprise an increase, in certain cases, in the number of tarsal segments, an increase in the antennal segments and the appearance of ocelli.

When the number of antennal segments is more than four in the adult, as for example in most genera of the Pentatomidæ, the second segment of the antennae apparently divides, thus increasing the number to five. In the Ectrichodiinæ (Reduviidæ) the antennae of the adults may have four, six, seven or eight segments, the neanides having four segments. The increase in this instance can be seen to be taking place at the fourth and fifth instars, in the apical segment.

An increase in the number of antennal segments in species of *Opistoplatys* Westwood 1834 (Reduviidæ-Tribelocephalinæ) is probably caused by the division of the apical segment but there is no information regarding this, since the neanidal stages of this genus and, indeed, any of the genera in this subfamily, have been studied hardly at all.

In the Hammacerinæ (Reduviidæ), represented in South America, the number of the antennal segments may be more than forty, *e.g. Hammacerus cinctipes* Stål 1858, or over thirty, *e.g. H. luctuosus* Stål 1854, but, curiously enough, the division into so many segments is restricted not to the apical segments but to the second segment.

Division into this large number of segments, which will eventually take place, is more or less clearly indicated in the neanide of the fifth instar in *H. gayi* Spinola 1852, a specimen of which I have examined. In species belonging to the genus *Homalocerus* Perty 1833 of the same subfamily, namely *maculicollis* Stål 1872, *varius* Perty 1833 and *binotatus* Champion 1899, there are approximately fifteen, seven and ten segments respectively forming the second segment.

Another instance of antennal modification as regards the form and not the number may be seen in the neanides of *Cletus* Stål 1859 (Coreidæ) which have the second and third segments expanded and flattened, but in the adult the segments are normal.

Other modifications which take place comprise the reduction in size or disappearance of spines or secretory hairs, the latter a characteristic of certain Reduviidæ.

Neanides sometimes possess remarkable structures which are lost in the final moult. An instance of this is the Mirid *Paracarnus myersi*

Fig. 2

Neanide of *Paracarnus myersi*
China 1931. Miridæ-Deræocorinæ (original, China).

China 1931 (Miridæ-Deræocorinæ)
(Fig. 2) and *Hoffmannocoris chinai*
Miller (Reduviidae-Rhaphidoso-
minae) (Fig. 38).

The legs also undergo a considerable alteration in form, especially the
anterior pair, the tibiæ of which in
the neanides may be greatly expanded, and become progressively
smaller in each instar and are normal in the adult, cf. *Anoplocnemis
phasiana* (Fabricius) 1781, *Ochrochira rubrotincta* Miller 1931 (Coreidæ-Coreinæ). Conversely, the neanide may have more or less normal
anterior tibiæ, which became expanded to a lesser or greater degree
in the adult, cf. *Petalochirus* Palisot Beauvois 1805 (Reduviidæ-
Salyavatinæ).

Legs that are strongly spinose in the neanide become less
strongly so in the adult in certain cases, cf. *Hoffmanocoris chinai*
Miller 1950 (Reduviidæ-Rhaphidosominæ) (Fig. 38). In *Scipinia
spinigera* Reuter 1881 of the same subfamily, a Javanese species, the
spines on the anterior tibiæ develop at the fifth instar.

The *fossula spongiosa* present in the adults of many Reduviidæ
appear usually at the fourth instar. The tarsi, usually composed of
two segments in the neanides, increase to three in most cases in
the adult stage.

With regard to the development of the hemelytra and metathoracic wings, it is usual for the rudiments to appear at the third
instar, and at the fifth instar they are often long enough to cover a
considerable portion of the abdomen. In genera in which both
alate and apterous adult forms occur, it is not always possible to
decide when the neanide has reached the fifth instar whether the
resulting adult will have wings or not, cf. *Marænaspis* spp. (Redu-
viidæ-Ectrichodiinæ).

Two or more forms exhibiting different degrees of wing development are to be found in several families. Thus the adult may have
fully developed wings (macropterous), have shortened wings
(brachypterous or micropterous) or may be wingless (apterous).

In certain Reduviid genera, namely *Edocla* Stål 1859, *Paredocla*
Jeannel 1914, and *Marænaspis* Karsch 1892, the males may be
alate or apterous, but the females are always apterous. Generally
the metathoracic wings are shorter than the hemelytra, and in the
case of brachyptery the former are more reduced proportionally.

Alary polymorphism is associated in the Heteroptera with modifications of the thoracic segments, chiefly the pronotum, reduction

in size or complete absence of ocelli and occasionally a tendency to physogastry.

It is not uncommon for apterous individuals to be mistaken for immature forms. To be able to decide, it is essential first to examine the apical abdominal segments. Other adult characters will be found in the number and structure of the antennal segments and in the absence of dorsal abdominal gland ostioles. In the adult these are indicated only by a feeble modification of the segmental margins mid-dorsally of certain segments.

Characteristic of the neanides of many families are the abdominal glands, the ostioles of which are situated at the basal margins of the fourth to sixth dorsal segments, sometimes on the fourth and fifth only or solely on the sixth. These glands, to which the names 'repugnatorial', 'stink' or 'odoriferous' are given on account of the odorous and volatile fluid they secrete—which apparently assures the possessor of a certain amount of protection against enemies—are situated below the integument of the abdomen dorsally.

It has been observed that neanides are able to project the fluid for some distance, but generally it flows from the gland and spreads over the insect until it has volatilized (*e.g. Ochrochira rubrotincta*).

In the adults, the glands are situated in the thorax with the ostiole between the meso- and metapleuron or in the metasternal depression adjacent to the inner margin of the acetabulum. When the ostiole is located between the meso- and metapleuron there is usually an evaporative area surrounding it, and its margins may be enlarged.

In the Reduviidæ the 'stink' glands in *Rhodnius prolixus* Stål 1859, and in *Triatoma rubrofasciata* (de Geer) 1773, were first discovered by Brindley. There are, however, two types of glands, those which are found in other families of Heteroptera as well as in the Reduviidæ and another type situated laterally at the base of the abdomen and under the first abdominal tergite; these have two small ostioles situated near the posterior angle of the metathoracic epimeron. This type of ostiole has been noted in the genera *Eupheno* Gistel 1848, *Cethera* Amyot and Serville 1843, *Cetheromma* Jeannel 1917, *Caprocethera* Breddin 1903, and *Centrocnemis* Signoret 1852. In *Eupheno*, however, the ostiole is situated on a somewhat complicated and lamellar elevation which forms the evaporative area.

The odour of the volatile fluid to the human sense of smell is generally repellent, but it is not always so, on account of its similarity to that of pineapple, cinnamon, ether, for example. The odour of the secretion from some Reduviidæ resembles that of valerianic acid.

The value of the ability to secrete a highly odorous fluid has yet to be assessed. It may be that it has some sexual significance in adults, but more probably it is mainly secretory. The fact that it does, on occasion, deter aggression does not necessarily indicate that its function is solely protective.

To refer again to the neanidal glands, the area surrounding the ostioles is more strongly sclerotized than the remainder of the integument and is termed a 'dorsal plate'. These plates are usually quadrate, trapeziform or elliptical in shape. In some species the plates may be conical, strongly convex or tuberculate.

In some of the Pentatomidæ sclerotized areas are present on all segments, but not more than three bear the ostioles of glands. In adult forms, although the dorsal abdominal glands are absent, vestiges of the ostioles are usually apparent, and by preparing specimens in KOH the presence of the vestigial gland sacs may sometimes be revealed.

References

Balduf 1941; Beament 1946, 1947; Berlese 1914; Brindley 1930; Butler 1923; Girault 1906; Grandi 1951; Gross 1901; Heidemann 1911; Heymons 1906; Hungerford 1922, 1923; Jorden 1932; Kershaw 1908, 1909, 1910; Kirkaldy, 1909a, 1909b; Leuckart 1835, Miller 1929a, 1929b, 1931b, 1932a, 1934, 1953a, 1953b, 1955; Readio 1926, 1927b; Slater 1951; Southwood 1949; Stroyan 1954; Usinger 1946, 1947; Walton 1936; Whitfield 1929, 1933; Wigglesworth 1954; Wigglesworth and Beament 1950; Wygodzinsky 1944, 1947b.

Chapter 3

THE LEGS OF HETEROPTERA

The legs of Heteroptera perform, apart from the act of locomotion, several other functions. For that reason it is considered appropriate to describe these functions and at the same time to bring to notice some of the remarkable modifications in the femora, tibiæ and tarsi of certain species.

In the first place, an important duty performed by the legs is that of cleaning the antennæ and rostrum from which dirt is removed by the anterior tibiæ which the bug holds together, drawing the parts to be cleaned between them. The body and wings are cleaned by being stroked by the anterior and posterior tibiæ, the former in some species having a small comb-like structure composed of short and moderately robust setæ, on the inner surface near the apex.

Female Heteroptera have been observed to rub and scrape with the posterior tibiæ the terminal segments of the abdomen. This is to remove vestiges of spermatozoal matter adhering after copulation has taken place, but it could possibly give the impression that the insect was stridulating.

As a rule the legs are used by the male to grasp the female prior to, during and sometimes after copulation. It is, however, not an invariable rule that the male continues to clasp the female at this time; in fact, when connexion has been satisfactorily made, it may release the female and orientate its body in the opposite direction, *more canum*.

Predatory species naturally use the anterior legs for seizing prey, the median legs sometimes assisting in the operation. Nevertheless, in species which are exclusively predaceous, for example those belonging to the Reduviidæ and Nabidæ, the form of the anterior legs does not invariably conform with the types known as raptorial. In one type the anterior femora and tibiæ have teeth or spines or abundant and somewhat robust setæ, on the lower surface.

The raptorial type of leg is a characteristic of the Emesinæ (Reduviidæ). In the Phymatidæ as well as in some aquatic Heteroptera, namely the Belostomatidæ, Nepidæ and the Gelastocoridæ, the anterior legs are modified to form another raptorial type in which the femur and tibia may have short denticles on the inner surface and the femur may be considerably produced apically, the produced portion forming one side of a pincers (Phymatidæ), or the anterior tibia may be provided with very abundant short setæ (Belostomatidæ, Nepidæ, Gelastocoridæ). The anterior tibæ of Enicocephalidæ are sometimes spined on the inner surface.

20

In some Reduviidæ and Nabidæ the anterior, and sometimes the median, tibiæ have a very useful structure known as the *fossula spongiosa* which covers the inner surface of the tibia to a varied extent.

Latreille, it would appear, was the first to note this structure, but he did not suggest what its function might be. Twenty-six years later, Dufour examined it, and gave it the name 'fossette spongieuse'. He stated, 'ce corps placé au dessus du tarse et d'une forme ovalaire est charnu, pulpeux et, à sa surface inférieure paraît au microscope couvert d'un duvet excessivement court semblable à celui du velours. C'est une véritable pelote spongieuse, un organ eminément fonctionel destiné à exercer l'acte du toucher et de la préhension, et adapté aux habitudes d'insecte habituellement chasseur'.

It is clear from the foregoing that Dufour had made a fairly thorough examination of the structure in both living and dead specimens, but, unfortunately, he did not emphasize the fact that it is only after the bug is dead and the structure has desiccated and is consequently shrunken that it can be termed a 'fossette'.

In 1837, Spinola, apparently unaware of Dufour's observations, drew attention to the 'fossette' and expressed his opinion as follows: 'Les tibias de plusieurs Réduvites ont un organe particulier qui m'a paru exercer une fonction analogue à celui d'une ventouse et que j'ai nommé pour cette raison, ventouse tibiale . . . Cette conformation a une certaine analogie avec les ventouses des sangsues qui sont étrangères a leur nutrition et qui ne le serve qu'adhérer étroitement aux corps qu'elles ont pris pour point de départ. Elle m'a paru remplir le même office dans nos Réduvites auxquelles elles prêtent un moyen facile de prendre une position verticale ou renverse, soit obliquement soit même horizontalement et de s'y maintenir en adhérant étroitement au corps solide, sans avoir besoin ni de le saisir ni de s'y cramponner'.

Ninety-two years afterwards, another observer (who had apparently overlooked the remarks of Spinola concerning the structure) concluded that it assisted the possessor to walk up a smooth surface and therefore must be a climbing organ. Later investigation, however, has demonstrated that the function of the 'fossette' is to increase the gripping capabilities of the legs.

Observation of an attack on, and the eventual overcoming of large and powerful arthropods such as Diplopoda by members of the subfamily Ectrichodiinæ (Reduviidæ), will confirm that without the *fossula spongiosa* the tibiæ of the attacker would not be capable of gripping the prey.

A remarkable departure from the usual methods of zoophagous Heteroptera for capturing prey is that practised both in the adult and neanidal stages, by the Reduviids *Amulius* Stål 1865 and *Ectinoderus* Westwood 1843 which are found in the Oriental Region. These Reduviids make use of resins (Malay-damar) produced by certain trees, in particular *Agathis alba* and *Pinus merkusii* which they smear on their anterior tibiæ. It is noteworthy that the resins selected do not harden very rapidly and thus retain their efficiency for a suitable period.

After having applied the resin, the Reduviid takes up a position on a tree-trunk with its body at an angle to the tree and often with its head directed downwards. It extends the tibiæ and waits until some small insects–usually bees of the genus *Trigona*–become entangled after the manner of a fly on flypaper.

This striking habit of making use of resin to capture insects was apparently first observed by Uittenboogaart in Surinam in 1901. In the course of collecting other insects, he found a *Beharus lunatus* Lepeletier and Serville 1825, on the trunk of a resin-producing tree. This species belongs to the subfamily Apiomerinæ.

Since he was in some doubt as to whether the glutinous substance with which the tibiæ were smeared had been purposely applied or whether it had been secreted by the insect, he removed it by washing the tibiæ in alcohol. He records that after the removal of the substance the Reduviid, in a short space of time, found another supply and plunged the anterior tibiæ in it.

What probably gave rise to uncertainty as to the origin of the substance in the case referred to, may have arisen from the fact that the other legs had some of it on them. Attention is drawn to this because, of the several species of Apiomerinæ examined by the writer, most of them had traces of the substance on the median and posterior legs and indeed, sometimes on the body.

The Malaysian species which belong to the Ectinoderinæ appear to be able to prevent the resin from coming into contact with the

---

Fig. 3 Legs of Heteroptera (facing)

1. *Scaptocoris talpa* Champion 1900. Cydnidæ-Cydninæ. Anterior tibia and tarsus.
2. *idem.* Posterior tibia.
3. *Carcinocoris bilineatus* Distant 1903. Phymatidæ-Carcinocorinæ. Anterior femur and tibia.
4. *Agreuocoris nouhalieri* Handlirsch 1897. Phymatidæ-Macrocephalinæ. Anterior femur and tibia.
5. *Holoptilus* sp. Reduviidæ-Holoptilinæ. Anterior leg.
6. *Anoplocnemis curvipes* (Fabricius) 1781. Coreidæ-Coreinæ. Posterior leg.
7. *Gorpis papuanus* Harris 1939. Nabidæ-Gorpinæ. Anterior leg.
8. *Acocopus verrucifer* Stål 1864. Coreidæ-Merocorinæ. Posterior leg.
9. *Spalacocoris sulcatus* (Walker) 1872. Lygæidæ-Blissinæ. Anterior leg.
10. *Megenicocephalus chinai* Usinger 1946. Enicocephalidæ. Anterior leg.
11. *Ectomocoris* sp. Reduviidæ-Piratinæ. Anterior leg.
12. *Stenolaemus* sp. Reduviidæ-Emesinæ. Anterior leg.

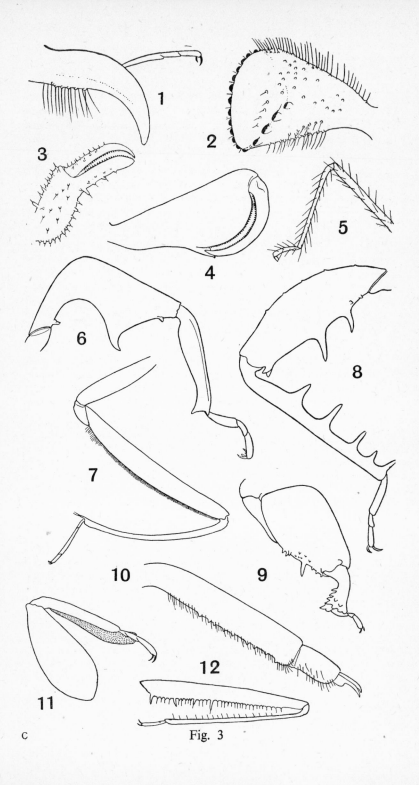

c

Fig. 3

other legs and with the body. In Malaya I removed the resin from the anterior tibiæ of *Amulius malayus* Stål 1866, and was able to observe the insect renewing the resin which it did by dipping the tibiæ in a small quantity of it. The resin in this case was from *Agathis alba*.

The Malaysian species do not use the anterior legs for locomotion and, furthermore, the tarsi are modified. In the South American Apiomerinæ the tarsi are fully developed, but the anterior legs are not used in walking.

There appears to be no information regarding the methods of predation by the Ethiopian genera of Apiomerinæ, *Cleontes* Stål 1874, *Diaspidius* Westwood 1857 and *Rhodainiella* Schouteden 1913. In the first-mentioned the anterior tarsi are lacking and in the others they are reduced and lie, when not in use, in a shallow sulcus at the apex of the tibia.

In phytophagous Heteroptera and in those that have wholly or partly abandoned a vegetable diet, the anterior legs are, as a rule, of simple structure. The median and posterior legs, however, may exhibit considerable diversity in shape and ornamentation.

Modifications to the anterior legs of *Spalacocoris sulcatus* (Walker) 1872 (Lygæidæ-Blissinæ), suggest that they perform a double function, predatory and fossorial, the femora and tibiæ being spined on the lower surface and the tibiæ also having sub-acute spines at the apex, directed, more or less, forwards.

Among the most striking differences in form between the median and posterior legs are those exhibited by many genera of the Coreidæ, for example, *Leptoglossus* Guérin 1830, *Anoplocnemis* Stål 1873, *Pachylis* Lepeletier and Serville 1825, *Sagotylus* Mayr 1865, *Petillia* Stål 1865, *Petascelis* Signoret 1847, *Carlisis* Stål 1858, *Acanthocephala* Laporte 1832, *Anisocelis* Latreille 1829, *Sulpicia* Walker 1871, *Holcomeria* Stål 1873, *Derepteryx* White 1837, *Priono-lomia* Stål 1873, *Phyllogonia* Stål 1873, *Plectrocnemia* Stål 1873, *Pternistria* Stål 1873, *Mygdonia* Stål 1865, and *Ochrochira* Stål 1883.

Fig. 4 *Legs of Heteroptera* (*facing*)

1. *Chelochirus* sp. Lygæidæ-Blissinæ. Anterior Leg.
2. *Diactor bilineatus* (Fabricius) 1803. Coreidæ-Acanthocephalinæ. Posterior tibia.
3. *Limnogeton expansum* Montandon 1896. Belostomatidæ. Anterior tibia and tarsus.
4. *Acanthocephala* sp. Coreidæ-Coreinæ. Posterior leg.
5. *Nerthra grandicollis* (Germar) 1837. Galgulidæ. Anterior leg.
6. *Lethocerus niloticum* (Stal) 1854. Belostomatidæ. Anterior leg.
7. *Petascelis foliaceipes* Distant 1881. Coreidæ-Coreinæ. Posterior leg.
8. *Sigara sjostedti* (Kirkaldy) 1908. Corixidæ. Anterior tibia and tarsus.
9. *Rhinocoris* sp. Reduviidæ-Harpactorinæ. Anterior leg.
10. *Sigara* sp. Corixidæ. Posterior tibia and tarsus.

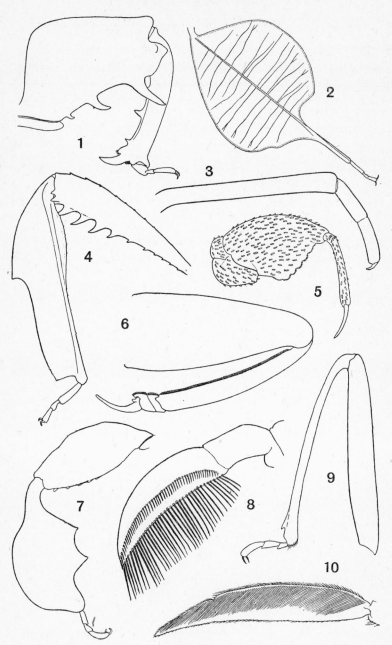

Fig. 4

In some of these genera the median tibiæ are also modified, being flat.

It should be noted that these striking structural modifications are present in the males only. The modifications in the posterior legs usually take the form of an enlarged femur with tubercles or spines on the lower surface and tibiæ with expansions or spines. In *Anisocelis*, *Diactor* Perty 1830, *Leptoglossus* and *Stenoscelidea* Westwood 1847 (*Placoscelis* Stål 1867) the posterior tibiæ are strongly foliaceous. The purpose, if any, of these extravagant modifications in form and ornamentation, however, remains a mystery.

Aquatic phytophagous Heteroptera, e.g. Corixidæ, have the anterior legs considerably modified and adapted for clasping food. In these legs the tarsi are fused into one segment, the pala. The other legs also perform different functions: the middle pair are adapted for clinging to some object or other; the posterior pair, of which the tibiæ have abundant setæ, are adapted for swimming.

Legs adapted to fossorial purposes are to be seen in a few genera only. An excellent example is offered by the genus *Stibaropus* Dallas 1851 (Cydnidæ), in which the anterior tibiæ are formed for use as scrapers while the posterior tibiæ serve to eject the soil which the bug excavates. These Heteroptera live among roots in the soil. The posterior tibæ are used in stridulation by those species that have a stridulatory organ on the ventral surface of the abdomen.

References
Amyot and Serville 1843; Champion 1898; Distant 1903; Dufour 1833, 1834; Gillett 1932; Latreille 1807; Miller 1938, 1939, 1942; Readio 1927; Spinola 1837; Weber 1930; Wigglesworth 1938, 1939.

Chapter 4

STRIDULATION

The ability to produce sounds by friction of one part of the body against another is possessed by many insects including the Heteroptera. It attains, however, the highest degree of efficiency in most of the Reduviidæ both in the adult and the more advanced neanidal stages. A stridulatory organ is also present and equally efficient in most of the Phymatidæ.

With regard to the Reduviidæ, the act of stridulation was first observed by Ray in the year 1710. Referring to *Reduvius personatus* Linnæus 1758, he wrote that it emits a sound not unlike that made by gràsshoppers, by rubbing its sternum with its beak. Two hundred years later, Handlirsch described in more detail how the sounds are produced and based his description on an examination of *Coranus subapterus* De Geer 1773. In the prosternal furrow of the Reduviid he found that there were 170 transverse striæ separated from each other by a space of 0.005 mm.

In the majority of species the width and the spacing of the striæ are more or less uniform, but in some genera of the subfamily Tribelocephalinæ the striæ are feebly developed and in others they are well-developed, widely separated from each other and few in number.

The genus *Stenolæmus* Signoret 1858 (Emesinæ) exhibits a somewhat different type of striated furrow. In *S. plumosus* Stål 1871 and *S. crassirostris* Stål 1871, the striæ become progressively coarser towards the posterior end of the furrow; in *S. marshalli* Distant 1903, *S. decarloi* Wygodzinsky 1947 and *S. bogdanovi* Oshanin 1870, the furrow is coarsely striate in the posterior half only.

Another type of striæ is to be seen in the Ethiopian genus *Afrodecius* Jeannel 1919 (Tribelocephalinæ). In this genus the sulcate part of the prosternum is somewhat arcuate and the striæ—also few in number—are of varied width.

Possession of a stridulatory furrow has been considered characteristic of the family Reduviidæ, but increased knowledge has shown that this concept is no longer valid. Some Ethiopian genera, namely *Diaspidius* Westwood 1857, *Cleontes* Stål 1874, *Rhodainiella* Schouteden 1913 (Apiomerinæ), *Phonolibes* Stål 1854 (Phonolibinæ) and *Aphonocoris* Miller 1950 (Harpactorinæ), also the Oriental genera *Amulius* Stål 1865 and *Ectinoderus* Westwood 1843 (Ectinoderinæ) have no striations in the furrow.

A stridulatory furrow is present in *Lophocephala* Laporte 1832, a genus of Phonolibinæ found in India. In the genus *Aulacogenia*

27

Stål 1870, Stenocephalinæ the striæ in the posterior two thirds of the furrow are coarse but in the remainder they are visible only under high magnification.

Phonolibes tricolor Bergroth 1912, an Ethiopian species, has a very long rostrum. It is straight and extends to the base of the abdomen; its apex, therefore, could not be brought into contact with striæ even if they were present.

The genus *Linshcosteus* Distant 1904 (Triatominæ), has no stridulatory furrow and the rostrum is much shorter than the head. Other genera of the Triatominæ in which this genus has been placed are provided with a striate prosternum.

The genera *Psophis* Stål 1863 and *Euvonymus* Distant 1904 (Reduviinæ) have the prosternum convex and no striæ.

There are indications that in the Oriental genus *Staliastes* Kirkaldy 1900, the striæ in the furrow appear to be degenerating and the rostrum appears to be becoming shorter. In this case also, contact is not possible between the rostrum and the striæ. In *Staliastes malayanus* Miller 1940 (Reduviinæ), striæ are absent and in other species of the genus, namely *rufus* Laporte 1832 and *zonatus* (Walker) 1873, the furrow is very narrow and has no striæ posteriorly. In the species in which striæ are present they are visible only under high magnification.

Campylorhyncha Stål 1874 (Tegeinæ) (Oriental Region), has the rostrum extended considerably beyond the posterior end of the prosternal furrow which has coarse striæ posteriorly.

In the majority of the Reduviidæ the prosternum in which the striated furrow is located, is not extended posteriorly beyond the anterior coxæ. The genera in which it is so extended are *Xenorhyncocoris* Miller 1938 (Ectrichodiinæ) and *Sava* Amyot and Serville 1843 (Harpactorinæ). It reaches well beyond the anterior coxæ. In both these genera the rostrum is very long. In *Pantoleistes* Stål 1853 (Harpactorinæ) the prosternum is rounded with an extremely narrow sulcus which apparently has no striæ.

A stridulatory apparatus is present in certain Pentatomidæ belonging to the subfamily Pentatominæ. This apparatus which has been termed a *macula stridulatoria* consists of an ovate, striate area on the fifth and seventh segments of the abdomen ventrally. The possessor stridulates by rubbing the posterior tibiæ–which are provided with short pegs–against it. Both sexes of *Tetyra* (Fabricius) 1803, *Pachycoris* Burmeister 1835, *Polytes* Stål 1867 have this apparatus.

A similar type of stridulatory apparatus is present in representatives of the subfamily Tessaratominæ (Pentatomidæ). On the first segment of the abdomen dorsally is an elliptical striate area and at the base of vein Cu of the metathoracic wings is a row of short ridges parallel to each other and in a more or less straight line.

Among the species having this type of apparatus are *Embolosterna taurus* Westwood 1837, *Hypencha opposita* Walker 1868, Malaysian species and *Eurostus validus* Dallas 1851 from China and Formosa. It is present in both sexes.

In the Scutellerinæ (Pentatomidæ) the genera *Sphærocoris* Burmeister 1835 and *Chiastosternum* Karsch 1898 have a stridulatory apparatus. The males of *S. testudo-grisea* (De Geer) 1778, a common and variable Ethiopian species, have the apical margin of the pygophore produced and flattened. On this flattened portion is a strigil composed of six or seven transverse rows of robust peg-like bristles, lying with apex directed backwards. It is assumed that the apex of the scutellum acts as a plectrum.

The employment of the antennæ in the production of sounds has been referred to by several observers who have stated that the Coreid *Phyllomorpha laciniata* de Villiers 1835 is able to produce sound by rapidly vibrating its antennæ. This phenomenon has also been recorded in respect of *Centrocoris spiniger* (Fabricius) 1781 and of *Spathocera laticornis* Schilling 1829. It is doubtful if sounds perceptible to the human ear could be produced by such feeble appendages as antennæ, however rapid and sustained the vibration. It is noteworthy that vibration of the antennæ may frequently be observed in neanides.

One species of Piesmidæ, *Piesma quadrata* (Fieber) 1861, according to Leston, is able to stridulate, the apparatus being a strigil situated on vein Cu of the metathoracic wing which is scraped against a ridge on a dorsal abdominal segment more or less as in those Cydnidæ which possess the faculty.

A stridulatory mechanism has been recorded for the Aradidæ by Bergroth, the species concerned being *Artabanus excelsus* Bergroth 1892. This consists of a rastrate area on each side of the third ventral segment. Esaki and Matsuda also described the same structure when drawing up their description of *Artabanus lativentris*, but they did not mention what other part of the insect constituted the plectrum. This, as pointed out by Usinger, is provided by the posterior tibiæ which have a fine file-like ridge on the inner posterior surface. Usinger has drawn attention to four types of stridulatory mechanism in addition to that possessed by *A. excelsus*. In *Strigocoris* Usinger 1954, the posterior margin of the segment has comb-like teeth on each side and the plectrum is the sub-apical enlargement of the posterior femur. *Pictinus* Stål 1873 has a similar apparatus except that the surface of the posterior margin of the second visible segment is modified and its surface is finely file-like rather than comb-like. A fourth type is present in the males only of *Illibius* Stål 1873. The second visible segment has a wide smooth area on each side of the middle. Across the middle of this area is a minutely striate arc. Stridulation is effected by the rubbing of a single peg located on the inner surface of the posterior femur. In *Aradacantha* Costa 1865 a wide, minutely grained arc crosses the metapleuron. In this genus a ridge on the inner face of the median femora acts as a plectrum.

An apparatus presumed to have a stridulatory function, present in the males only of *Nabis flavomarginatus* Scholtz 1846, has a row of robust curved setæ near the apex of the abdomen. By rubbing these setæ with the posterior tibiæ the bug has been said to produce sounds, although the investigator himself had been unable to hear them. This Nabid was observed to rub the apex of the abdomen first with one tibia and then with the other, a motion which may be observed often in other insects; for example flies, beetles and also other Hemiptera. The object is not to produce sounds but to remove particles of fæces or other unwanted substances.

In the case of *Nabis flavomarginatus*, the male only was concerned and the deduction was that the motion produced sounds for the purpose of attracting the female which, nevertheless, was not observed to react in the expected manner.

An unusual modification of the surface of the hemelytra which is possibly a component of a stridulatory organ, is to be seen in *Ptenidiophyes trinitatis* China 1946, of the family Dipsocoridæ. Lying obliquely to the apex of the corium is a deep longitudinal fissure, and along the inner margin of an elongate oval thickened area incorporating two veins and the area between them towards the bottom of the fissure, there is a row of ten pegs projecting from the costal side and extending to the other side. Stridulation would be effected, probably by rubbing this area with the posterior tibiæ.

Both sexes of the aquatic bug *Plea minutissima* Leach 1817, are able to produce sounds. In this species the stridulatory apparatus is formed by part of the posterior margin of the prosternum which fits into a depression in which are fine striæ. By moving the prosternum backwards and forwards the bug produced sound, but more than one bug must stridulate simultaneously for it to be audible to the human ear.

Other families of aquatic Heteroptera contain sound-producers. In the Corixidæ, Notonectidæ, and Nepidæ only the males have a stridulatory apparatus, but both sexes of the Veliidæ possess one. Male Corixids are able to produce sounds of varying pitch sometimes resembling chirping and at other times the sound of a knife being rubbed against a hone. The explanation as to why the tones change is probably that the pala is armed with short teeth and the anterior femora with short spines. Both these parts of the anterior legs are rubbed against the transversely-grooved labrum, the toothed pala producing one type of note and the spined femora another.

Kirkaldy, remarking on the stridulatory organs in *Corixa*, states that they 'are so diversely formed that it is possible to distinguish the various species (in the male sex) from an examination of those organs only. This is, I believe, unique, up to the present, among the Rhynchota.'

In *Naucoris cimicoides* Linnæus 1761, Handlirsch discovered that on the dorsal surface of the abdomen of the male only there were two finely striate areas which he considered formed the plectrum of a stridulatory organ. Stridulation in this case was effected by friction between them and the apical margin of the preceding segment. Since this organ is present in the male only, he considered that the sounds produced were for the purpose of attracting the female.

Stridulation has been reported to occur in the Nepidæ but definite information regarding this is lacking. Bueno and Hungerford have stated that in a species of *Ranatra* there is present on the external surface and near the base of the anterior coxæ a low elevation, and on the inner surface of the pronotum a ridged area. Friction between these two parts is said to produce sounds.

In conclusion, it must be pointed out that, although there is an appreciable amount of information on the sound-producing capabilities of Heteroptera, a satisfactory explanation of the phenomenon is not yet forthcoming. The fact that in some instances both males and females are able to stridulate as well as neanides, means that the probability of its having a sexual significance can be ruled out. Furthermore, the act is performed in varied circumstances: during copulation or when the insect is disturbed, for example. Again, it may occur for no apparent reason.

It seems clear, therefore, that stridulation is solely a nervous reaction and, with the possible exception of the Corixidæ, in the males and females of which a tympanal organ is present, there is no evidence that the sounds are perceived mutually.

References

Bergroth 1892; Esaki and Matsuda 1951; Handlirsch 1900a, 1900b; Horvath 1894; Kirkaldy 1901; Leston 1952a, 1954a; Muir 1907; Olivier 1899; Saunders 1893; Schneider 1928; Usinger 1954.

Chapter 5

NATURAL ENEMIES OF HETEROPTERA

Heteroptera, in common with other insects, are liable to be attacked by various enemies of which the most important are hymen-opterous parasites of the ova, belonging to the families Scelionidæ, Eupelmidæ and Braconidæ. I have also observed a wasp—*Polybia rhaphigaster* Saussure devouring the ova of *Eusthenes robustus* Lepeletier and Serville 1825 (Pentatomidæ-Tessaratominæ) in Malaya.

Ants, too, must be numbered among the foes from which even large and robust species with a relatively tough integument rarely escape alive; if they do, they will have been severely mutilated. Mammals, birds and reptiles also are enemies but there is rela-tively little information regarding the extent to which Heteroptera suffer from their attacks.

It would appear that on account of the odorous fluid which most Heteroptera, both neanidal and adult, are able to secrete, attacks by vertebrates would occur infrequently, but the ability to produce an apparently disagreeable fluid does not invariably ensure pro-tection. The victim, therefore, although not killed and devoured, is likely to suffer injury sufficient to cause eventual death.

Although there is a good deal of information on the general food of insectivorous mammals, no specific instances of their eating Heteroptera have been recorded. Monkeys are known to have a mixed vegetable and animal diet which includes insects, any kind of which are probably accepted. It has not been possible to find any references of insects–particularly Heteroptera–being eaten by wild monkeys.

Experiments have been carried out in which Heteroptera have been offered to captive animals, but since the conditions of such tests are artificial, it is not reasonable to expect trustworthy results indi-cating the likes or dislikes of an animal.

Nocturnal species of Heteroptera are probably captured by bats, but there is no available information on the subject. Accumulations of insect remains in sheltered places to which bats go to consume the insects captured during flight have been exhaustively examined by the writer on several occasions in Southern Rhodesia but no heteropterous fragments were found among the wings, legs and other portions of Orthoptera, Coleoptera and Lepidoptera which had been rejected and were lying on the floor. It has to be recog-nized, nevertheless, that very many Heteroptera are small and have a delicate integument. It is possible that those snapped up by a bat would be entirely devoured.

Heteroptera are eaten by birds quite frequently. This fact has been revealed by the examination of stomach contents of birds from various parts of the world and, as will be seen from the following examples, they are all capable of secreting an odorous substance.

The stomachs of thirty-three species of birds in North America were found to contain recognizable remains of adults and neanides of Pentatomidæ including *Brachymena tenebrosa* Walker 1867, *B. quadripustulata* (Fabricius) 1775, *Chlorochroa sayi* Stål 1872, *C. uhleri* Stål 1872, *C. ligata* (Say) 1831, *Thyanta custator* (Fabricius) 1803, *Peribalus abbreviatus* (Uhler) 1872, *Euschistus inflatus* Van Duzee 1904, *E. variolanus* Palisot Beauvois 1805, *Acrosternum hilaris* (Say) 1831 and *Carpocoris remotus* Horvath 1907. In addition to these neanidal and adult forms, a large number of ova was also found.

An American bird which has been recorded as feeding on Heteroptera is the sage sparrow *Amphispiza nevadensis*. In stomachs of this species, representatives of the Pentatomidæ, Lygæidæ, Nabidæ and Miridæ were found. In India the Pentatomid *Nezara viridula* Linnaeus 1758, a species which secretes a highly odorous fluid, has been found in the crops of *Dicrurus ater*, *Graculus macii*, *Oriolus melanocephalus*, *Acridotheres ginginianus* and *Francolinus vulgaris*.

To give one more example of a bird as a predator of Heteroptera, it was reported to the writer on one occasion in Malaya that the crop of a jungle fowl *Gallus bankiva* had been found to contain in addition to vegetable matter a large number of the Pentatomid *Tetroda histeroides* (Fabricius) 1798, a common pest of rice in the Oriental Region. This species has a relatively hard integument and also secretes an odorous fluid.

From these examples it is evident that the fluid does not repel insectivorous birds in every instance. Shore birds and those birds which frequent ponds and marshes occasionally capture Heteroptera, mostly aquatic kinds such as Corixidæ.

With regard to reptiles, large numbers of insects are consumed by lizards but there are few records of Heteroptera being eaten. Examination of the stomachs of certain African lizards has disclosed the remains of Pentatomidæ (*Sciocoris sp.*), Coreidæ, Lygæidæ (*Dieuches* sp.) and Reduviidæ (*Ectomocoris quadrimaculatus* Serville 1831). These Heteroptera had been devoured by the common Scincid *Mabuia striata* (Ptrs.).

There is only one record known to the writer of Heteroptera being eaten by a snake. This concerned a cobra *Naia tripudians* which he dissected. In its gut there were the remains of an unidentifiable Pentatomid as well as portions of beetles and ants.

The odorous secretion in some instances is, however, effective in repelling an enemy. Repulsion has been observed by the writer in Malaya when geckoes (*Hemidactylus frenatus*) were stalking insects on the walls and ceilings of houses at night when the lights were on. At certain times of the year the Cydnid *Geotomus pygmæus* Dallas 1851, is attracted to artificial light in large numbers in buildings and is an intolerable nuisance since it falls into food and drink rendering them unfit for consumption. The odour of the fluid of this bug is reminiscent of that of castor oil. During hunting, a gecko often seized a *Geotomus* but immediately rejected it. The bug is usually partially crushed, however.

Toads have been reported to eat occasionally the so-called squash bug *Anasa tristis* (De Geer) 1773 (Coreidæ) and *Euschistus fissilis* Uhler 1872 (Pentatomidæ). Aquatic Heteroptera are often preyed upon by fish (trout) in the stomachs of which remains of Gerridæ, Notonectidæ and Corixidæ have been found. Terrestrial kinds have also been discovered in the stomachs of fish, but it is probable that they were captured or swallowed when dead after having fallen accidentally into the water.

In addition to hymenopterous parasites, Heteroptera also have other insect enemies belonging to other Orders which either kill them outright or destroy them slowly. Internal parasites belong to this category.

It has been reported that cockroaches will eat bedbugs, but experiments have shown that this is only partially true. In experiments conducted with the object of ascertaining whether cockroaches would actually prey on bedbugs, the conclusion was reached that this bug was not eaten to any great extent. Under natural conditions it is probably never an item in the varied diet of the cockroach.

The bedbug, nevertheless, is a prey of the Reduviid *Reduvius personatus* Linnæus 1758, the fairly widely-distributed Palæarctic species and also probably of another Reduviid *Vesbius purpureus* Thunberg 1784, a much smaller and brightly-coloured species, confined to the Oriental Region. The probability that this Reduviid preys on the bedbug occurred to the writer during a prolonged stay in an internment camp in Sumatra. There, bedbugs were present in countless thousands and the only other insect found with them was *V. purpureus*.

Vesbius purpureus is often to be found beneath the floor-boards of Malay-type dwellings. In this situation many spiders and cockroaches are frequently present, but *Vesbius* does not appear to prey on them. Attempts to rear this Reduviid in the laboratory, by supplying spiders and cockroaches for food, failed; as did other attempts with lepidopterous larvæ. Of the several species of *Vesbius*, this species appears to be the only one associated with man and, in consequence, may be distributed by his agency. An instance of this has come to notice in the discovery of *V. purpureus* in Zanzibar, whither it had probably been carried by dhow from India.

Reduviidæ are almost entirely general feeders and they also attack other Heteroptera both in the neanide and adult stages. Incidentally, cases of cannibalism in this family have frequently been reported.

Other enemies of the Heteroptera are the Lygæid *Geocoris pallens* Stål, var. *decoratus* Uhler 1877, predaceous on the false cinch bug in America, the Melyrid beetle *Collops quadrimaculatus* Fabricius, which feeds on the ova of *Blissus leucopterus* (Say) 1832, the water-bug *Notonecta undulata* Say 1832, a predator of the ova of *Belostoma* (*Zaitha*), *flumineum* Say 1832, and Diptera, among which gall-midges (Cecidomyidæ) enemies of Tingidæ and tachinids, among which *Alophon nasalis* Bezzi, which attack Pentatomidæ and Pyrrhocoridæ.

Strepsiptera have been noted as attacking *Antestia* (Pentatomidæ), an important pest of coffee in East Africa and were responsible for rendering infertile from 20 to 80 per cent of the population of this insect. The effect of stylopization is to make the male incapable of fertilizing the female.

Other insect predators of Heteroptera include dragonflies, Asilidæ (sometimes known as robber flies) and Gryllidæ, namely *Gryllulus domesticus* Linnæus and *Gryllodes sigillatus* Walker (Orthoptera) which have been observed feeding on adults and ova of *Aphanus littoralis* Distant 1918 (Lygæidæ). Spiders are general feeders and will devour any Heteroptera which may be entrapped in their webs.

Mites are often found on Heteroptera, notably certain Reduviidæ among which *Velitra rubropicta* Amyot and Serville 1843 (Reduviinæ) and other species. Those most frequently selected by mites appear to pass a considerable part of their life under the loose bark of trees. It is not thought, however, that the mites are parasitic, but that phoresy is the reason for their presence.

Several species of Coreidæ and Lygæidæ have been found to be harbouring flagellates (*Herpetomonas*) in the gut and body fluid and, as is well known, pathogenic trypanosomes are found in most species of Triatominæ (Reduviidæ). These organisms, like the mites, are apparently innocuous. Other organisms found in the bodies of Heteroptera which are most probably injurious are nematodes.

References

Banks 1938; Conradi 1904; Corbett and Miller 1933; Cott 1934; van Deventer 1906; Frost and Macan 1948; Jourdan 1935; Kirkpatrick 1935-36; Knowlton 1944; Knowlton and Nye 1946; Kunckel d'Herculais 1879; Mason and Maxwell-Lefroy 1912; Mckeown 1934; Miller and Pagden 1941; Milliken and Wadley 1922; Poisson 1930 a and b; Severin and Severin 1910; Taylor 1945,

Chapter 6

HETEROPTERA ASSOCIATED WITH MAMMALS AND BIRDS

In the families Reduviidæ and Cimicidæ are to be found species associated with man, other mammals and birds. The universally-distributed and best known of these is undoubtedly the bedbug *Cimex lectularius* Linnaeus 1758, with its unpleasant odour and disagreeable habits. It thrives mostly in ill-kept dwelling houses and also in some tropical hospitals where hygiene is not always given the attention it deserves. In concentration camps where large numbers of persons are herded together the bedbug finds conditions ideal and therefore is able to increase more or less without check on account of the fact that it is rarely possible to apply adequate control measures.

By far the most important Hemiptera associated with man and which affect his well-being are some of the Triatominæ, all of which are distributed in North and Central America and the West Indies with the exception of the tropicopolitan *Triatoma rubrofasciata* (De Geer) 1773, and the less abundant species *Triatoma migrans* Breddin 1903, recorded from Sumatra.

It was during the voyages of explorers about two hundred years ago that attention was first drawn to *Triatoma* species on account of their attacks on sleeping persons. It was not until 1909, however, when Chagas, working at the Instituto Oswaldo Cruz in Rio de Janeiro, discovered that these Reduviidæ were vectors of trypanosomes; he stated that their transmission took place when the bug was feeding and that the infective stages of the trypanosome were located in the salivary glands.

This was eventually disproved by Brumpt who demonstrated that the life-cycle of the trypanosome is completed in the hind gut of the bug and that the trypanosomes are present in the fæces which the bug ejects at the time of feeding or soon after.

If the person bitten, when scratching the site of puncture which irritates on account of the injected saliva, rubs fæcal matter into it, or if fæces are introduced into an abrasion of the skin, or come into contact with the conjunctiva of the eye or mucous membrane of the mouth, entry of the trypanosomes into the blood stream takes place. Mammal reservoirs of the trypanosomes include armadillos, bats, opossums, wood-rats and squirrels.

Another Reduviid, *Apiomerus pilipes* (Fabricius) 1787 (Apiomerinæ) and the Cimicids, *Cimex lectularius*, *C. hemipterus* Fabricius 1803, *C. stadleri* Horvath 1912, and *Oeciacus hirundinis* (Jenyns)

1839 and the Lygæid *Clerada apicicornis* Signoret 1863, have also been proved to be vectors of trypanosomes.

According to Usinger, although Triatominæ may feed on many other vertebrates, most of them have definite host preferences, while a few, namely *Mestor megistus* (Burmeister) 1835, *Triatoma infestans* (Klug) 1834, and *Rhodnius prolixus* Stål 1859, in South America, also *T. phyllosoma* (Burmeister) 1835, in Mexico, have so adapted themselves to conditions in houses occupied by human beings that they may be regarded as domestic parasites.

In some instances, the host relationships are unique; for example, the South American genus *Psammolestes* Bergroth 1911, is associated with a bird of the family Dendrocolaptidæ, *Phacelodomus rufifrons* (Wied); another, *Cavernicola pilosa* Barber 1937, is associated with bats in Panama and Brazil. *Belminus rugulosus* Stål is associated with a sloth in Costa Rica. Among other species of Triatominæ, *Rhodnius prolixus* is found commonly with human beings but, under natural conditions, on armadillos and *Cuniculus paca* (Linnæus).

Other records of the association of Hemiptera with mammals include that of *Polydidus armatissimus* Stål 1859, discovered by the writer in the nest of a shrew, *Crocidura cærulea* Linnæus in Malaya, and those of various species of Cimicidæ (*Cacodmus* spp.) on birds and bats, of the Reduviid *Lisarda* Stål 1859 found in sheep-folds in Southern Rhodesia, and of *Clerada nidicola* Bergroth 1914 (Lygæidæ), in the nest of an opossum in Australia.

Regarding *Lisarda* sp., when it was observed for the first time, in sheds where sheep were housed, the first impression was that it was there for the purpose of attacking sheep. Unfortunately the initial observation was not followed by further investigation. It is more probable that the Reduviid was preying on termites.

Certain Hemiptera which belong to predominantly phytophagous groups have been observed to probe human skin as if they were attempting to suck blood. Recorded cases of this kind are relatively few and are confined to the Cydnidæ, Lygæidæ and Miridæ, all of which, so far as is known, are plant-feeders, but the Miridæ include many predaceous species.

In most of the instances in which phytophagous species have acted in this manner, it is probable that they were primarily in search of moisture and had been attracted by the odour of perspiration. In endeavouring to imbibe this they pierced the skin to some extent. Hemiptera behaving thus must therefore be regarded as facultative blood-suckers and considered as taking the first step towards the adoption of carnivorous habits.

Myers, in discussing the biting of man by Hemiptera of normally

phytophagous habits, has concluded that 'the vast majority of bites
... are by insects under the influence of unusual conditions, amount-
ing in extreme cases, as during attraction by electric light, to a
complete extraction from their normal environment. The mere fact
of alighting on a large vertebrate body, whether accidentally or in
flight from beating or other collecting operations, brings the phytophagous insect within a range of a host of stimuli, visual, thermal,
tactile, olfactory, which are totally foreign to it'.

In discussing the association of insects and human beings it will
not be out of place to give a few instances of the consumption by
man of certain Heteroptera. As one example of this, the Pentatomid
Encosternum (*Haplosterna*) *delagorguei* Spinola 1852, is collected
by natives in Southern Rhodesia. They roast and eat the bugs either
alone or mixed with other kinds of food. Other Pentatomids, namely
Aspongopus nepalensis Westwood 1837, *A. chinensis* Dallas 1851, and
Erthesina fullo (Thunberg) 1783, have been recorded as items in the
diet of certain Asian peoples. The giant water-bug *Lethocerus indicum*
(Lepeletier and Serville) 1825, is considered a delicacy by the Laos
of Indo-China, and the ova of several species of Corixidæ are
collected by Mexicans; these ova are eaten by wealthy and poor
people. The Pentatomid *Euschistes zopilotensis* Distant 1890, as
well as many other Heteroptera, are extensively used as food in
Mexico.

References

Bacot 1921; Bergroth 1914; Blanchard 1902; Bodenheimer 1951; Brumpt 1912,
1914a, 1914b; Cuthberston 1934; Lent 1939; Miller 1931a; Myers 1929;
Usinger 1934, 1944.

PART 2

FAMILIES OF THE HETEROPTERA

PART 2

FAMILIES OF THE HETEROPTERA

PLATASPIDAE Dallas 1851, *List Hem.* 61. (Plate 1)

This family comprises large to very small, highly convex and shining insects, many of which are pests in varying degrees of importance of cultivated plants, mainly Leguminosæ. (cf. *Coptosoma* Laporte 1832, and *Brachyplatys* Boisduval 1835).

The members of this family are characterized by the greatly enlarged scutellum which entirely covers the hemelytra (except the basal external area of the corium) and the metathoracic wings, and leaves only the connexival segments of the abdomen partly visible. The hemelytra and metathoracic wings when at rest are folded under the scutellum more or less after the manner in which the metathoracic wings are folded under the elytra of Coleoptera.

Coptosomoides China 1941, *Bozius* Distant 1901 and *Tiarocoris* Vollenhoven 1863 have the labrum enlarged forming a small, membranous chamber into which the setæ are partly coiled. The setæ are long, for the reason, it is supposed, that members of these genera feed on mycelia of fungi which penetrate somewhat deeply into decaying wood. This supposition is based on the fact that Aradidæ and Meziridæ also are mycetophagous and possess similar long setæ which, however, are coiled in the head capsule.

A curious feature of the genera *Severiniella* Montrouzier 1894, *Elapheozygum* Kuhlgatz 1900, and of *Ceratocoris* White 1841, is the tuft of closely arranged short setæ on the ventral surface of the seventh abdominal segment.

In colouration the Plataspidæ show a considerable range from unicolorous metallic greenish-black, brown, whitish or black with yellow or white vermiculation or spots.

Sexual dimorphism is exhibited by some genera, the head of males bearing one or two projections anteriorly. In the genus *Ceratocoris* there are two projections either short or long with the apex acute; in *Elapheozygum* there are also two projections but each is irregularly furcate apically, while in *Severiniella* there is one long projection with the apex bifurcate. The head of the females has no structural features.

In *Triodocoris* Miller 1955 a dimorphic genus, the males have both the juga and vertex produced and lamellar; the female is normal. Other dimorphic genera are *Teuthocoris* Miller 1955 and *Glarocoris* Miller 1955, the males of which have the juga produced. There are three genera which differ considerably from other

41

genera of the Plataspidæ. They are *Probænops* White 1842, an Ethiopian genus which has a dull, not glabrous integument and the pronotum gibbose anteriorly; *Bozius* Distant 1901, with a dull integument and also a strongly punctate pronotum and scutellum; *Tropidotylus* Stål 1876, similarly punctate but also coarsely rugose. The last two genera are from India.

Very little is known about the developmental stages of Plataspidæ. The ova of *Brachyplatys subæneus* Westwood 1837 and also some of its neanidal instars have been described and figured. This species deposits its ova in groups with the longer axis parallel to the substratum. The developmental stages of this species and also of *Coptosoma cribraria* (Fabricius) 1798, have been described by Kershaw.

The ovum of *Probænops obtusus* Haglund 1894, is sub-ampulliform with the opercular end strongly oblique. The side in contact with the substratum is very feebly rounded.

Plataspis flavosparsa Montandon 1894 places its ova in two rows, each ovum alternating with the ovum opposite. They are covered by the female with a secretion deposited in the form of elongate pellets which harden. According to Carayon this secretion comes from a portion of the differentiated gland on the mid-intestine.

Regarding the hemelytra and metathoracic wings, to facilitate folding of the former, the vein R is transversely constricted in many places; the metathoracic wing when at rest has the basal lobe only folded under.

In the genera *Apotomogonius* Montandon 1892, *Triodocoris*, *Ceratocoris* and *Gelastaspis* Kirkaldy 1902, vein 2A of the metathoracic wing has short, transverse pegs or ridges in the basal part which is somewhat thicker than the remainder of the vein. These pegs would appear to constitute the plectrum of a stridulatory apparatus. Since, however, the anal lobe of the wing is folded under when the wing is in the resting position and covers the vein, the pegs could not come into contact with another part of the body which might bear a strigil. The function of these pegs is therefore obscure.

The distribution of the family embraces mainly the Ethiopian, Oriental, Australian and warm areas of the Palæarctic Regions, but principally the Ethiopian Region where most of the strikingly dimorphic forms occur.

References

China 1931; Kershaw 1910; Carayon 1949a.

CYDNIDAE Billberg 1820, *Enum. Ins.* p.70 (Plate 1)

The Cydnidæ are mostly black, piceous or light-brown in colour with a shining and usually punctate integument. Although most of them are small, there are some moderately large genera, namely *Scaptocoris* Perty 1830, *Ectinopus* Dallas 1851, *Prolobodes* Amyot and Serville 1843 (Neo-tropical), *Cyrtomenus* Amyot and Serville 1843 (Nearctic and Neotropical) *Scoparipes* Signoret 1879 (Malaysian), *Adrisa* Amyot and Serville 1843 (Australian), *Plonisa* Signoret 1881 (Ethiopian) and *Brachypelta* Amyot and Serville 1843, which is widely distributed. Some species of *Cydnus* (Fabricius) 1803–another also widely distributed genus–are also large. There is another genus, *Sehirus* Amyot and Serville 1843, species of which are entirely violaceous or have yellowish spots and are distributed in the Palæarctic and Nearctic Regions.

The Cydnidæ mostly live in the soil and their food is mainly roots of plants and animal matter. *Geotomus pygmæus* Dallas 1851 and *Cydnus indicus* Westwood 1837, probably feed on grass roots and the former has been found on rice seedlings. The female of *Legnotus limbosus* Geoffroy 1785, has been recorded as depositing ova in a cavity in the soil and remaining with them, apparently without feeding, for fifteen-twenty days.

The legs in some genera are formed for digging, and in *Scaptocoris talpa* Champion 1900 the posterior tibæ have no tarsi; the anterior and median legs, however, are normal. In *Stibaropus* Dallas 1851, in which the anterior legs are also fossorial, tarsi are present and the apical and lateral margins of the tylus and juga respectively are tuberculate and have short, robust, acute spines. These parts of the head are similarly modified in *Scaptocoris* and *Chilocoris* Mayr 1864.

In *Syllobus* Signoret 1879, *Lactistes* Schiödte 1848 and *Brachypelta*, the anterior margin of the head is dorso-ventrally compressed and somewhat recurved. Modifications such as these suggest a function similar to that performed by the legs.

Facultative blood-sucking has been noticed in *Geotomus pygmæus*, the secretion from the thoracic glands of which has an odour resembling that of castor oil. This species is a troublesome pest from time to time, on account of large numbers invading dwellings to which they have been attracted by artificial light.

All the genera and species mentioned belong to the subfamily **Cydninæ.**

There are four subfamilies: **Corimelæninæ** Uhler 1872; **Cydninæ** Dallas 1851; **Canopinæ** Horvath 1919; and **Megaridinæ** McAtee and Malloch 1928.

44   THE BIOLOGY OF THE HETEROPTERA

Corimelæninæ Uhler 1872; these are small shining insects with a large scutellum covering the hemelytra except the strongly sclerotized costal margin.

Cydinæ Dallas 1851, are mostly small or moderately sized insects with a flattened scutellum which is small and does not extend to the apex of the corium. Representatives of the **Cydninæ** are widely distributed; the **Corimelæninæ** live under stones, in mammalian excreta or on plants; the **Cydninæ** live mainly in the soil and feed on roots.

Canopinæ Horvath 1919, of which there is only one known genus, *Canopus* (Fabricius) 1803, are ovate convex insects. The head and pronotum have slightly reflexed margins. Corium carinate costally and showing one definite longitudinal vein; pronotum with a median longitudinal impressed line anteriorly and a more or less defined transverse impression, in or along which are punctures. The scutellum covers the hemelytra entirely except for the external area of the corium basally.

Megaridinæ McAtee and Malloch 1928 also contains one genus *Megaris* Stål 1862. Species of the genus are small, ovate or subcircular in outline, highly convex; anterior margin of the head and anterior and lateral margins of the pronotum carinate and slightly reflexed; the apex of the head is more or less emarginate. Nothing appears to be known about the ecology of either the **Canopinæ** or the **Megaridinæ**.

References

Miller 1931 a; Thomas 1954.

PENTATOMIDAE Leach, 1815,

Brewster's Edinburgh Encyclopædia, **9**, 121 (Plate 1)

This is one of the most important families of the Heteroptera. It contains more than 2,500 species and a very great number is still awaiting description. Some species are of economic importance: among these are *Nezara viridula* Linnæus 1758, which has a wide range of food plants and causes considerable damage to the rice crop from time to time, *Solubea poecila* (Dallas) 1851 and *Mormidea ypsilon* Linnæus 1767, also pests of rice. Both these and *N. viridula* attack the ripening ears when they are in the 'milk' stage.

The Pentatomidæ are characterized (with exceptions) by the horizontal head, the lateral margins of which conceal the site of insertion of the antennæ which usually have five segments, by a well-developed scutellum, odoriferous glands in both larvæ and adults and tarsi with three segments with arolia.

On the whole, Pentatomidæ have a robust integument and exhibit an appreciable diversity in colouration which includes black, brilliant red, yellow, metallic green or blue. Sculpturation consists chiefly of puncturation and some species have spines on the head, body and legs, for example, *Scotinophara* Stål 1867 (**Podopinæ**), *Aspavia* Stål 1865 (**Pentatominæ**), *Carbula* Stål 1865 (**Pentatominæ**), *Hoploxys* Dallas 1851 (**Asopinæ**), *Leptolobus* Signoret 1835 (**Asopinæ**).

Some members of the **Tessaratominæ** are among the largest of the family and several of them have a striking appearance with the lateral pronotal angles strongly produced. Among these may be mentioned the genera *Mucanum* Amyot and Serville 1843, *Embolosterna* Stål 1870, *Pygoplatys* Dallas 1851, and *Amissus* Stål 1863, all distributed in the Malaysian sub-region.

In this subfamily also the meso- and metasternum and the third abdominal segment are abnormal in certain genera. For example, in *Lyramorpha* Westwood 1837, *Oncomeris* Laporte 1832, and *Plisthenes* Stål 1864, the third segment of the abdomen is strongly and acutely produced medially, the produced part extending to the anterior coxæ. In *Piezosternum* Amyot and Serville 1843, the mesosternum is produced and forms a wide, thick carina which extends to the anterior coxæ; the anterior part of this carina is compressed on each side.

Mucanum has the metasternum produced forming a robust carina which extends almost to the apex of the bucculæ. The anterior end is rounded and projects outwards somewhat. The mesosternum is medially elevated so that the rostrum is displaced to one side. In *Embolosterna* the modifications are similar.

In *Siphnus* Stål 1863, the metasternum is produced and extends to the anterior coxæ. It is directed outwards anteriorly but the mesosternum is not elevated, being concave medially, so that the rostrum may lie in its normal position. The meso- and metasternum in *Hypencha* Amyot and Serville 1843 and in *Pygoplatys*, are similarly modified. The rostrum in all these genera is relatively short.

Some genera are notable on account of their brilliant colouration; for example, *Mattiphus* Amyot and Serville 1843, and *Carpona* Dohrn 1863, from the Indo-Oriental Region, (**Tessaratominæ**) *Callidea* Laporte 1832 and *Procilia* Stål 1864, Ethiopian genera (**Scutellerinæ**).

In the main, Pentatomidæ are phytophagous, with the exception of the **Asopinæ** which, so far as records show, are entirely carnivorous. The best known of these are *Cantheconidea furcellata* Wolff 1801, which attacks the larvæ of the Zygænid moth *Artona catoxantha* Hampson, an important defoliator of the coconut palm in the Oriental Region; *Perilloides bioculatus* (Fabricius) 1775, which attacks the Colorado beetle in the United States of America; *Zicrona coerulea* Linnæus 1758, predaceous on *Haltica coerulea* Oliver (Coleoptera) in the Malaysian sub-region and on other insects elsewhere, since it is widely distributed, having been recorded from many localities in the Palæarctic Region; *Oechalia consocialis* (Boisduval) 1835, a species found in Australia which preys on the larvæ of *Phalenoides glycine* (vine moth) and on *Galerucella semipullata* (fig-leaf beetle) and *Picromerus bidens* Linnæus, a Palæarctic species reported to feed on a variety of insects, including larvæ of butterflies and moths. Hemerobiidæ and Coleoptera. It has also been recorded as feeding avidly on the bedbug when enclosed in a room infested by these pests.

According to Weber these predaceous Pentatomids are not eager to attack any but slow-moving insects which are not equipped to defend themselves. The method of attack also differs from that adopted by other predaceous Hemiptera, for example the Reduviidæ, which use their anterior legs to seize their prey and then insert their stylets into a part of the body where the integument is softer, namely, between the abdominal segments, into the mouth or coxal cavities.

The **Asopinæ** rely primarily on the paralizing effect of the saliva which they inject into their prey before seizing it with the legs. None of the Asopinæ has legs of the raptorial type, consequently it is not difficult to understand that they are not prone to attack lively and vigorous insects able to protect themselves.

The genera *Cazira* Amyot and Serville 1843 and *Cecyrina* Walker 1867, both belonging to the Asopinæ, have modified anterior legs but they are not of the raptorial type.

The habitats of Pentatomidæ are mainly the foliage and stems of plants or among roots. Other habitats which have come to notice are vegetable debris and flood refuse for *Eumenotes obscura* Westwood 1847 (**Eumenotinæ**) stems of a grass (*Imperata*) for *Megarrhamphus* Laporte 1832 (**Phyllocephalinæ**) and among stems of growing rice for *Tetroda histeroides* (Fabricius) 1798 (**Phyllocephalinæ**) and for *Scotinophara coartata* (Fabricius) 1798 (**Podopinæ**). Both *T. histeroides* and *S. coarcata* are important pests of rice.

Pentatomidæ may also be pollinating agents. One record of this is referred to by Distant who stated that he had received information that *Cantao ocellatus* Thunberg 1784 (**Scutellerinæ**) which occurs on the 'moon tree' (*Macaranga roxburghi*) in India is a diurnal and very active species. The tree is said to depend for pollination entirely on this insect which conveys pollen to the stigma on its legs, rostrum and spines.

A tendency to swarm, a factor regulated mainly by the food

supply it would seem, has been observed in respect of *Nezara viridula* (**Pentatominæ**), *Tetroda histeroides* and *Scotinophara coarctata* congregating in rice fields: *Encosternum* (*Haplosterna*) *delagorguei* Spinola 1852 (**Tessaratominæ**) appears in large numbers at certain periods of the year in Southern Rhodesia and is collected and eaten by natives.

Swarming and periodic migration occurs with *Eurygaster integriceps* Puton 1881 (**Scutellerinæ**), pest of wheat in Asia Minor. In this species, development proceeds in the lowlands, then the adults migrate to upland regions where they hibernate; they return to the plains for reproductive purposes.

The female Pentatomids usually deposit their ova in groups on part of the host-plant, but occasionally on some object nearby. They attach them to the substratum with a glutinous substance and when the act of oviposition is completed the female departs.

There are, however, certain Pentatomidæ, the females of which have been stated to remain on or near the group of ova until the neanides have hatched. The purposes of this unusual behaviour lack a logical explanation.

Behaviour of this kind is often interpreted as being a manifestation of maternal solicitude. Such an interpretation, however, is surely an example of the loose manner in which some observers endow organisms which are very low in the scale of development with the sentiments of animals much higher in the scale.

This peculiar habit has certainly nothing to do with the incubation of the ova and furthermore, it can have no protective value against adverse climatic conditions or against potential enemies, hymenopterous parasites and the like. A possible explanation seems to be that it is a persistence of the gregarious habit which may have been more usual formerly, a habit which still persists in varying degrees in a few species.

The assumption that maternal solicitude is exhibited when a female remains with the egg-mass, is based on an observation by Dodd, in respect of *Tectocoris lineola* (Fabricius) 1781 var. *banksi* Donovan 1805 (**Scutellerinæ**). This observer recorded that *Tectocoris* clasped the group of ova which it had deposited on a plant stem and moved its position only when some object approached, the direction to the right or left depending on the angle of approach. An analogous reaction may be observed in Delphacidæ (Homoptera), Reduviidæ and also Buprestidæ (Coleoptera) at rest on a grass-stem or on a twig.

A further objection may be advanced as to the reality of the so-called protective attitude and maternal solicitude of female bugs. This objection is, that if the female in most if not all reported instances has not been under close examination without intermission during the entire period of incubation, which is not likely to be much less than ten days, it cannot be accurately affirmed that the bug has not moved at all from the spot during that period.

Dodd stated, however, that 'it is absolutely certain that "broody bugs" remain foodless during the whole period of three weeks or more of sitting; they occupy the same position always and various investigators have failed to reveal any puncture in the twigs in front of them'.

That a bug might remain without food for a period of weeks cannot be denied but the question must be put: Which group of ova would have the 'protection' of the female in view of the likelihood that more than one group of ova is produced, the second batch following before the hatching of the first?

Some species of Pentatomidæ are very prolific and, so far as is known, deposit their ova in groups of varying numbers with the longer axis vertical to the substratum; but at least one exception, in which the longer axis of the ovum is in a parallel position, is to be seen in the method of deposition of ova by *Megymenum brevicorne* (Fabricius) 1787 (**Dinidorinæ**). Other species of this genus and probably of allied genera deposit their ova in this fashion.

The deposition of a constant number of ova sometimes occurs. It has been observed in the large species *Pycanum ponderosum* Stål 1854 (**Tessaratominæ**) depositing fourteen, always in the order three-four-four-three, and the same number and order have been recorded for *Pentatoma rufipes* Linnæus 1758 (**Pentatominæ**).

The ova are usually placed on the leaves or branches of the host-plant or on some object in the vicinity. Eclosion is effected by the embryo pushing off the operculum; before it can do this is has to loosen it. It is assisted in this process by the 'egg-burster', a highly sclerotized part of the embryonic cuticle This piece of apparatus usually has the shape of an elongate, flattened rod expanded at one or both ends and the other surface of which has a short, conical projection (Fig. 1). The manner in which this apparatus is used in removing the operculum is set forth in detail in the chapter on development.

The neanides of Pentatomidæ, which pass through five instars during the course of development, do not resemble the adults very closely except as regards the shape of the head and legs. In colour they differ entirely from the adults.

An appreciable number of ova has been described and, in some cases, figured. From the knowledge at present available it is possible to state that the ova of representatives of the **Pentatominæ, Asopinæ, Dinidorinæ** and **Graphosomatinæ** are mostly cylindrical with or without chorionic processes, and those of the **Scutellerinæ** and **Tessaratominæ** spherical or ovate; chorionic processes are sometimes present in the ova of the former.

In view of the fact, however, that an immense number of ova remains to be described, it would be unwise to dogmatize but to await the results of further investigation which may confirm or deny this. Some examples of Pentatomid ova are given in Fig. 8.

Both adults and neanides in Pentatomidæ are able to secrete an odorous volatile fluid, the adult from the metathoracic glands with the ostiole and evaporative area situated between the meso- and metapleura, the neanides from glands lying under the dorsum of the abdomen.

The part of the integument in which the ostioles of the abdominal glands are situated is highly sclerotized and usually has the form of an elliptical or trapezoidal plate. These ostiole-bearing plates known as 'dorsal plates' are on the third, fourth and fifth segments. In some species other segments have sclerotized plates but they do not bear ostioles. This may indicate, however, that formerly more than three segments bore gland ostioles.

The odour of the secretion produced by the glands is not always of a kind that is unpleasant to human beings, but this, of course, is an individual matter. Its action, too, is not always repellent to other organisms. It is not always possible to state to what other odour it can be likened, but various odours have been suggested, for example, those of almonds, pineapple, castor oil or rotting apples.

The fluid, on being secreted from the glands, spreads over the area around the ostiole or further, according to how copious the the discharge is. It then volatilizes somewhat rapidly, and should it come into contact with the human skin it usually leaves a stain resembling that made by iodine.

It is necessary to point out that the ostiole of adults in certain genera can be seen only with difficulty, since the peritreme is lacking and is barely larger than the surrounding puncturation.

There are eleven subfamilies of Pentatomidæ: **Asopinæ** Spinola 1850, **Tessaratominæ** Stå 1864, **Eumenotinæ** Esaki 1922, **Cyrtocorinæ** Distant 1880, **Dinidorinæ** Stål 1870, **Phyllocephalinæ** Dallas 1851, **Pentatominæ** Stål 1864, **Tahitocorinæ** Yang 1935, **Scutellerinæ** Leach 1815, **Podopinæ** Dallas 1851 and **Serbaninæ**.

Asopinæ Spinola 1850, are all predaceous and are characterized by the horizontal head and the basally thickened rostrum; the bucculæ are short which enables a more extensive lateral movement of the rostrum. In some species the anterior tibiæ have a short, acute spine on the lower surface.

Tessaratominae Stål 1864, are mostly large or very large with a normal rostrum and scutellum.

Eumenotinæ Esaki 1922 contains one genus only, *Eumenotes*, characterized by the more or less compressed body, antennæ with four segments, the scutellum extending to the fourth abdominal segment and the tarsi with two segments.

Cyrtocorinæ Distant 1880, are small, obscurely coloured insects of somewhat bizarre habitus; one species, *C. monstrosus* Germar 1839, has the juga and the lateral margins of the pronotum strongly produced and a very large scutellum which covers a greater part of the membrane and bears a long, thick, irregularly shaped spine. The connexival segments are also strongly produced; in other species the parts referred to are much less produced.

Dinidorinæ Stål 1870, are mostly moderately large, black or brown insects with a yellow or red connexivum which is often spotted. The antennæ have five segments with the apical segment somewhat compressed in some species; the rostrum is short, not extending beyond the mesosternum and often much shorter; basally the scutellum is wide, apically rounded.

Phyllocephalinæ Dallas 1851, are moderately large, elongate or elliptical in outline with the head acute anteriorly, the juga in some species separated; pronotum transverse with the postero-lateral angles produced in some genera; the rostrum is mostly short and extends just beyond the anterior margin of the prosternum, but in some genera it is longer.

Pentatominæ Stål 1864, has five segments in the antennæ, a triangular scutellum which is shorter than the abdomen and also does not conceal the corium or clavus; the basal rostral segment lies in a sulcus on the ventral surface of the head.

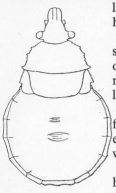

Tahitocorinæ Yang 1935, are small, apterous, strongly punctate with pedunculate eyes, no ocelli; cimicoid in outline; the ostioles of the metathoracic glands are very small and a little larger than the punctures.

Scutellerinæ Leach 1915, with the antennæ of five segments and with the scutellum covering entirely or partly the abdomen and the wings when they are at rest.

Podopinæ Dallas 1851, with the thorax hexagonal, sometimes spined, the head anteriorly produced, the eyes very prominent, pedunculate and the antennæ more or less clavate.

Fig. 5
Tahitocoris cheesmanae
Yang 1935.

Serbaninæ Lester 1953. Antennæ with four segments; head, pronotum and connexival segments with foliaceous expansions.

ACANTHOSOMIDAE Stål 1864,

Hem. Afr. **1,** 33 and 219 (Plate 1)

Formerly placed in the Pentatomidæ as a subfamily. Representatives are characterized by the tarsi having two segments, the third abdominal segment spinously produced midventrally, the mesosternum with a median laminiform carina and the seventh abdominal segment of the males in some genera spinously produced. The produced portion of the third abdominal segment overlaps the posterior end of the sternal carina, both ends thus in contact being obliquely truncate. In some cases the sternal carina extends almost to the apex of the head. The antennæ have four or five (mostly) segments.

The Acanthosomidæ are widely distributed and have been recorded from Africa, India, Java, the Philippine Is., Australia, parts of the Palæarctic Region and from Mexico.

Acanthosoma hæmorroidalis Linnæus 1758 and *Clinocoris* (*Elasmostethus*) *griseus* Linnæus 1758, have been recorded feeding on carrion. Cannibalism has also been known to occur.

APHYLIDAE Bergroth 1906, *Zool. Anz.*, 29

Small, dull-coloured, strongly convex insects with piceous puncturation and brownish reddish suffusion. There is only one genus known up to the present: this is *Aphylum*, of which there are two species, *syntheticum* Bergroth 1906 and *bergrothi* Schouteden 1906.

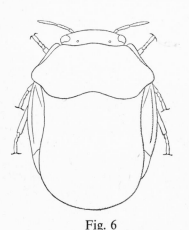

Fig. 6

Aphylum syntheticum Bergroth 1906. (Aphylidæ)

The Aphylidæ are similar in habitus to the Plataspidæ but are not glabrous as are most of that family. They may also be distinguished by the strongly punctate pronotum and scutellum and by the shape of the pronotum, the lateral angles of which are lobately produced posteriorly and the postero-lateral margin strongly angulately incised.

The meso- and metanotum are visible from above, the former as a lobe in the angulate incision of the posterior margin and the latter as a segment immediately behind the lateral pronotal angles. Furthermore, the corium (exposed part) is highly sclerotized and resembles the scutellum in structure. Its costal margin is widely separated at the base from the body margin.

The antennæ have five segments, the tarsi three and the femora are somewhat compressed laterally with the apical part of the lower surface somewhat sulcate.

Aphylum has been recorded so far only from Australia and nothing is apparently known of its habits.

UROSTYLIDAE Dallas 1951, *List Hem.* 313 (Plate 1)

This small family is distributed mainly in the eastern Palæarctic Region, the Malay Peninsula and Australasia. It was formerly considered to be a subfamily of the Pentatomidæ.

Two species, *Urochela distincta* Distant 1900 and *U. falloui* Reuter 1888, have been reported as pests, the former on account of its

---

Plate 1 (facing)

Plataspidæ, Cydnidæ, Pentatomidæ, Acanthosomidæ, Urostylidæ, Phlœidæ.

1 and 2. *Ceratocoris cephalicus* Montandon 1899. Plataspidæ.
3. *Libyaspis wahlbergi* (Stål) 1863. Plataspidæ.
4. *Severiniella cameroni* Distant 1902. Plataspidæ.
5. *Cantharodes jaspideus* Fairmaire 1858. Plataspidæ.
6. *Plonisa tartarea* Stål 1853. Cydnidæ-Cydninæ.
7. *Deroplax nigrofasciata* Distant 1898. Pentatomidæ-Scutellerinæ,
8. *Poecilocoris nigricollis* Horvath 1912. Pentatomidæ-Scutellerinæ.
9. *Solenostethium liligerum* Thunberg 1783. Pentatomidæ-Scutellerinæ.
10. *Chrysophara excellens* (Burmeister) 1834. Pentatomidæ-Scutellerinæ.
11. *Eumecopus longicornis* Dallas 1851. Pentatomidæ-Pentatominæ.
12. *Cinxia limbata* (Fabricius) 1803. Pentatomidæ-Pentatominæ.
13. *Carpona imperialis* Dohrn 1863. Pentatomidæ-Tessaratominæ.
14. *Caura marginata* Distant 1880. Pentatomidæ-Pentatominæ.
15. *Vulsirea variegata* Drury 1773. Pentatomidæ-Pentatominæ.
16. *Chalcocoris anchorago* Drury 1782. Pentatomidæ-Pentatominæ.
17. *Pygoplatys lancifer* Walker 1861. Pentatomidæ-Tessaratominæ.
18. *Leptolobus eburneatus* Karsch 1892. Pentatomidæ-Asopinæ.
19. *Edessa cornuta* Burmeister 1885. Pentatomidæ-Pentatominæ.
20. *Runibia decorata* Dallas 1851. Pentatomidæ-Pentatominæ.
21. *Urusa crassa* Walker 1868. Pentatomidæ-Dinidorinæ.
22. *Alcaeus varicornis* (Westwood) 1842. Pentatomidæ-Pentatominæ.
23. *Megymenum quadratum* Vollenhoven 1868. Pentatomidæ-Dinidorinæ.
24. *Anaxandra* sp. Acanthosomidæ.
25. *Urostylis farinaria* Distant 1901. Urostylidæ.
26. *Urostylis striicornis* Scott 1876. Urostylidæ.
27. *Phloea corticata* Drury 1773. Phlœidæ.

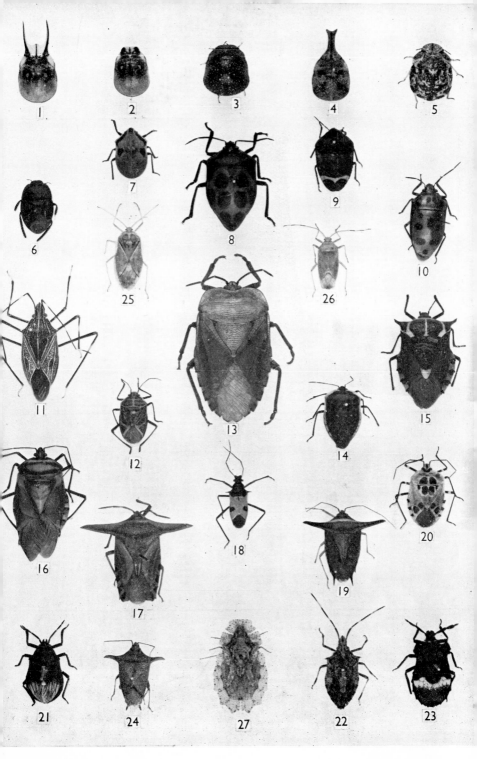

Plate I

being a nuisance when it appears in large swarms and the latter because of its destructive activities to pear trees, grape vines and other plants in China. Apart from this information, little is known about the habits and developmental stages of species belonging to this family.

Most of the Urostylidæ are somewhat small insects, mainly pale greenish or greenish-brown in colour and with a relatively delicate integument.

The ova of *Urostylis farinaria* Distant 1901 and of *Urolabida khasiana* Distant 1887, which were obtained by dissection by the writer, are oval, with three closely sited long filamentous chorionic processes at the upper end. There is no operculum, so apparently the chorion is split by the embryo at the time of eclosion.

The presence of such processes similar to those on the ova of certain Miridæ (cf. *Helopeltis* Signoret 1858) suggests that the ova are inserted by the female into a soft substance such as decaying vegetable matter or even into the shoots of plants. On the other hand the female may embed them in the soil.

References

Miller 1953; Yang 1936.

PHLOEIDAE Dallas 1851 *List Hem.* **1,** 149 (Plate 1)

This family contains two genera only. They are characterized by the strong foliaceous expansions of the head, pronotum and connexivum, antennæ composed of three segments which are concealed by the pronotum, and the dorso-ventrally compressed habitus.

The rostrum is long and extends to about the middle of the ventral surface of the abdomen.

Phlœidæ are found mainly on the trunks of trees, the bark of which they are said to resemble to some extent.

The ova which are cylindrical and white are deposited by the female in fissures in bark. Apparently the ovum has no operculum or egg-burster.

A good many apparently superficial observations have been made on the habits of Phlœidæ and according to them, the females remain with the ova and when the neanides hatch they cluster about her and do not leave until they are more mature.

The two genera *Phloea* Lepeletier and Serville 1825 and *Phloeophana* Kirkaldy 1908 are Neotropical.

References

Brien 1930; Leston 1953; Perez 1904.

COREIDAE Leach 1815,
Brewster's Edinburgh Encyclopœdia **9,** 121 (Plate 2)

This is a large family comprising many diverse forms. It reaches its highest stage of development in the tropics, where it is represented by many genera. The Coreidæ have the antennæ situated on the upper part of the sides of the head; they are composed of four segments. The pronotum is commonly trapeziform but may have the angles spinose or foliaceous. Trichobothria are present on the ventral abdominal segments. The ostioles of the metathoracic glands are very distinct.

Genera with pronotal modifications include members of the subfamily **Coreinæ,** namely, *Derepteryx* White 1829, *Holcomeria* Stål 1873, *Prionolomia* Stål 1873, *Phyllogonia* Stål 1873, *Holopterna* Stål 1873, *Evagrius* Distant 1901, *Petillia* Stål 1865, *Dalader* Amyot and Serville 1843 and *Acanthocephala* Laporte 1832. Both the lateral margins of the abdomen and pronotum are very strongly foliaceous and spinose in *Phyllomorpha* Laporte 1832, *Pephricus* Amyot and Serville 1843 and *Craspedum* Amyot and Serville 1843. These genera, also of the **Coreinæ,** are the most bizarre representatives of the family.

Generally speaking, the hemelytra are complete, but brachypterous forms also occur. Of these may be mentioned *Typhlocolpura* Breddin 1890, *Lygeopharus* Stål 1870 **(Coreinæ),** *Psotilnus* Stål 1859, *Micrælytra* Laporte 1832, *Dulichius* Stål 1865 **(Alydinæ),** *Chorosoma* Curtis 1830 and *Jadera* Stål 1860 **(Rhopalinæ).**

One apterous genus known so far, is the Australian *Agriopocoris* Miller 1953, of Aradid-like appearance, which was discovered among leaf debris on the floor of the forests and under bark **(Agriopocorinae).**

Ocelli are present in the Coreidæ. The scutellum is small and always shorter than the abdomen. Some tropical species exhibit striking modifications of the posterior femora and tibiæ, the former being very greatly enlarged, sometimes spinose and tuberculate and the latter may have either foliaceous expansions or spines.

In colour the Coreidæ are mostly brown, yellowish brown or stramineous. There are, however, some genera, for example, *Anisocelis* Latreille 1829 **(Coreinæ),** which have both body and legs brightly coloured. Others, namely, *Spathophora* Amyot and Serville 1843 **(Merocorinæ),** *Machtima* Amyot and Serville 1843, *Pachylis* Lepeletier and Serville 1825, and *Golema* Amyot and Serville 1843 and also some species of *Mictis* Leach 1814 **(Coreinæ),** are brown with a red or yellow pattern.

Metallic green species in which the colour may be due to the presence of scales or to the sculpture of the integument are found in the genera *Mictis*, *Petalops* Amyot and Serville 1843, *Phthia* Stål 1862, and *Sphictyrtus* Stål 1859 (**Coreinæ**). Dull black or piceous genera include *Hygia* Uhler 1861 and *Typhlocolpura* (**Coreinæ**).

Coreidæ possess 'stink' or 'repugnatorial' glands, the fluid from which is usually pungent. One is often made aware of the presence of Coreidæ by their odour, although the insects themselves may not be visible; for example, in grassy areas and rice-fields where species of *Leptocorisa* Latreille 1825 (**Alydinæ**) are present in large numbers.

The adults and neanides, in certain cases, are able to project the fluid for a short distance, but as a rule, when secreted, it spreads over the greater part of the body before volatilizing.

All Coreidæ are apparently phytophagous. They attack various parts but mainly the younger shoots and the leaves. The result of their attacks is the wilting and, if the attack be prolonged, the demise of the plant. This is caused by the saliva which is injected at the time of feeding.

Many Coreidæ attack cultivated plants but they may not necessarily be pests of economic importance. Some genera, however, are definitely in the category of pests. Among these are species of *Leptocorisa* which cause important damage to rice grains when they are in the 'milk' stage; *Theraptus* Stål 1859 and *Amblypelta* Stål 1873, reported to cause excessive nut-fall in coconut palms, and *Leptoglossus* Guerin 1836, a pest of many cultivated plants, including Cucurbitaceæ. (**Coreinæ**).

The genera *Physomerus* Burmeister 1835, *Anoplocnemis* Stål 1873 (**Coreinæ**), and *Riptortus* Stål 1859 (**Alydinæ**), include species that are occasional but less serious pests.

Gregarious tendencies have been observed in *Physomerus*, *Petascelis* Signoret 1847 (**Coreinæ**) and others. When such congregations occur it is not uncommon to see all stages of the bugs at one time.

Coreidæ oviposit on various parts of the host-plant, the ova being arranged in groups of varying size, in chains; or they are deposited singly. The arrangement may vary according to the conformation of the substratum.

Sometimes the female secretes a wax-like substance in granular or powder form which covers the exposed part of the ovum. (cf. *Mictis tenebrosa* (Fabricius) 1787) and allied genera. (**Coreinæ**).

An exceptional mode of oviposition has been recorded: in this the female places the ova on the male and they remain in this position until eclosion takes place.

This mode has been noticed in *Phyllomorpha laciniata* de Villers

E

1835, a Palæarctic species, found, according to some authors, on foliage and under stones and leaves. It also occurs on Gramineæ and herbaceous plants.

It should be remarked, however, that both the male and female have been observed to have ova on their backs. This would suggest that the presence of ova on both sexes was fortuitous, the ova having fallen from a female which happened to be near. Closer and repeated observations on ovipositing females of this species would, no doubt, throw more light on this apparently aberrant mode of oviposition.

Costa Lima records that a male specimen of *Plunentis porosus* Stål 1859 (**Coreinæ**), examined by him, had several ova adhering to the ventral surface of the abdomen and among them a recently emerged neanide without doubt belonging to the same species.

Coreidæ are mostly active insects and fly readily when disturbed. So far as is known, in general they do not take up a particular attitude when resting. One example, however, of a definite resting attitude is exhibited by *Hypselopus annulicornis* Stål 1855 (**Alydinæ**). A specimen shown on Plate 2, (31) mounted in the resting position was received from Dr. E. Burtt from Tanganyika Territory.

Knowledge regarding the developmental stages of Coreidæ is relatively scanty.

With the exception of the ova of *Anoplocnemis, Derepteryx, Euagonia* Dallas 1852 (**Coreinæ**), and of some other large genera which have a comparatively tough chorion, the ova of many genera have a somewhat delicate chorion. An operculum is generally present and, so far as is known, an egg-burster. Those egg-bursters which have been examined are in the form of an arcuate rod with the centre enlarged. (Fig. 1).

Investigations up to the present time show that the ova of Coreidæ are of several widely different types, the most common being cylindrical, truncate at each end or ovate with the side which is in contact with the substratum flattened. Some ova have on the flattened side a short pedicel.

Peculiar forms are exhibited by the ova of species of *Choerommatus* Amyot and Serville 1843, and of *Catorhintha mendica* Stål 1870 (**Coreinæ**). These are oblong cubical with the sides somewhat concave.

Other aberrant forms may be seen in the ova of certain *Rhopalinæ*. For example, those of *Corizus rubricosus* Bolivar 1879, are ovate with the opercular end oblique and with a short process on the operculum; those of *Myrmus miriformis* (Fallen) 1807 and *Liorhyssus hyalinus* (Fabricius) 1794, similar, but with a short process on the chorion below the opercular suture as well as on the operculum. These processes are apparently analogous to the chorionic processes on ova of Pentatomidæ and function similarly.

The six subfamilies of Coreidæ are: **Merocorinæ** Stål 1870; **Rhopalinæ** Amyot and Serville 1843; **Alydinæ** Dallas 1852; **Coreinæ** Stål 1867; **Pseudophloeinæ** Stål 1867; and **Agriopocorinæ** Miller 1953.

Merocorinæ Stål 1870 have strongly incrassate posterior femora, flattened and spined posterior tibiæ, the lateral angles of the pronotum more or less acutely produced and with the scutellum normal, horizontally produced and with a vertical elevation.

Rhopalinæ Amyot and Serville 1843. Small species with, in some cases, the interveinal areas of the corium hyaline.

Alydinæ Dallas 1852 usually have the head wider than the pronotum, the posterior angles of which are sometimes spinously produced and the posterior femora spined on the lower surface.

Coreinæ Stål 1867 contains some genera of bizarre appearance as *Phyllomorpha* and *Pephricus:* the head is narrow and the antennæ usually slender, but some of its segments may be expanded; this subfamily also contains some of the largest and conspicuous genera.

Pseudophloeinæ Stål 1867 are somewhat setose without a sulcus on the head and with the basal antennal segments shorter than the head; the posterior femora have tubercles and long spines and the seventh abdominal segment is produced.

Agriopocorinæ Miller 1953. Micropterous; antennal tubercles together about as wide as the head; ostioles of metapleural glands distinct; posterior acetabula not excised; bucculæ long, extending beyond the insertion of the antennæ; pro- and mesosternum sulcate; spiracles close to margin of abdomen, those on segments two and three marginal and visible from above.

References

Bolivar 1894; Costa Lima 1940; Miller 1929 b, 1953 c; Poisson 1930; Reuter 1909; Saunders 1893; Stroyan 1954.

HYOCEPHALIDAE

Bergroth 1906, *Zool. Anz.* **29,** 649.

This family contains one genus, *Hyocephalus* Bergroth 1906, from Australia. The characters are: head elongate, scutellum small; hemelytral membrane with four veins enclosing three large cells and then becoming branched. The seventh abdominal segment of the female is furcate. The tarsi have three segments, claws and arolia.

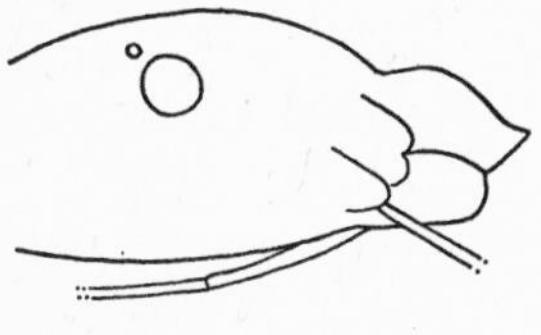

Fig. 7

Hyocephalus aprugnus Bergroth 1906. (after Bergroth) (Head). (Hyocephalidæ).

There is one species, *H. aprugnus* Bergroth 1906, described from a female.
Nothing is known about the ecology of this family.

LYGAEIDAE Schilling 1829, *Beit. z. Ent.* **1**, 37. (Plate 3)

A moderately large family of mostly sombre-coloured insects, but also containing some species which have bright colours, mainly red and yellow. The Lygæidæ are characterized by having the membrane of the hemelytra with four to five veins, three-segmented tarsi and the anterior femora sometimes incrassate and spined. The antennæ are inserted below the lower margin of the eyes. Alary polymorphism occurs.

There is not a great deal of knowledge about the ecology of the Lygæidæ or about their developmental stages, except of those species economically important.

Fig. 8 (*facing*)

Ova of PLATASPIDÆ, PENTATOMIDÆ, ACANTHOSOMIDÆ, PHLŒIDÆ, UROSTYLIDÆ, COREIDÆ, LYGÆIDÆ, PYRRHOCORIDÆ, VELOCIPEDIDÆ, PIESMIDÆ (*facing*)

1. *Probaenops obtusus* Haglund 1895. 1.60 mm. Plataspidæ.
2. *Brachyplatys vahlii* (Fabricius) 1787. ·80 mm. Plataspidæ.
3. *Megarrhamphus truncatus* Westwood 1837. 1·60 mm. Pentatomidæ-Phyllocephalinæ.
4. *Halyomorpha viridescens* (Walker) 1867. 1·50 mm. Pentatomidæ-Pentatominæ.
5. *Dryptocephala brullei* Laporte 1832. 1·50 mm. Pentatomidæ-Podopinæ.
6. *Mecidea* sp. ·70 mm. Pentatomidæ-Pentatominæ.
7. *Aspongopus* sp. 1·80 mm. Pentatomidæ-Dinidorinæ.
8. *Serbana borneensis* Distant. 2·00 mm. Pentatomidæ-Serbaninæ.
9. *Phloea corticata* Drury 1773. 2·60 mm. Phlœidæ.
10. *Urostylis farinaria* Distant 1901. ·80 mm. Urostylidæ.
11. *Urolabida khasiana* Distant 1887. 1·00 mm. Urostylidæ.
12. *Spartocera fusca* Thunberg 1783. 2·00 mm. Coreidæ-Coreinæ.
13. *Sciophyrus* sp. 1·60 mm. Coreidæ-Coreinæ.
14. *Liorhyssus hyalinus* (Fabricius) 1794. ·70 mm. Coreidæ-Rhopalinæ.
15. *Corizus rubricosus* Bolivar 1879. 1·00 mm. Coreidæ-Coreinæ.
16. *Pephricus livingstoni* Westwood 1857. 1·70 mm. Coreidæ-Coreinæ.
17. *Myrmus miriformis* (Fallen) 1807. 1·10 mm. Coreidæ-Rhopalinæ.
18. *Sephena limbata* Stål 1862. 2·40 mm. Coreidæ-Coreinæ.
19. *Euagona diana* Dallas 1852. 3·00 mm. Coreidæ-Coreinæ.
20. *Acanthosoma brevirostris* Stål 1873. 1·00 mm. Acanthosomidæ.
21. *Choerommatus* sp. 1·00 mm. Coreidæ-Coreinæ.
22. *Catorhintha mendica* Stål 1870. 1·20 mm. Coreidæ-Coreinæ.
23. *Dieuches* sp. 1·50 mm. Lygæidæ-Rhyparochrominæ.
24. *Aphanus littoralis* Distant 1918. 1·20 mm. Lygæidæ-Rhyparochrominæ.
25. *Nysius inconspicuus* Distant 1903. 1·40 mm. Lygæidæ-Lygæinæ.
26. *Antilochus nigripes* Burmeister. Pyrrhocoridæ.
27. *Scotomedes alienus* (Distant) 1904. 1·70 mm. Velocipedidæ.
28. *Piesma quadrata* Fieber 1844. ·64 mm. Piesmidæ.

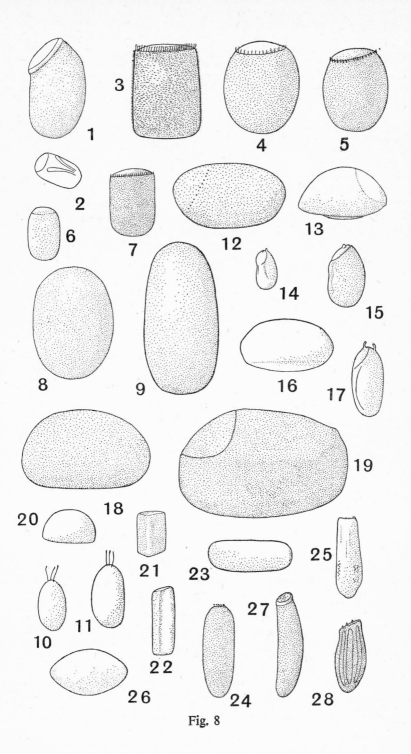

Fig. 8

The ova of a few species have been studied. *Nysius inconspicuus* Distant 1903 (**Lygæinæ**), produces a cylindrical ovum with short chorionic processes and with the base depressed; the ovum of *Aphanus littoralis* Distant 1918 (**Rhyparochrominæ**), is similar but it appears to be deposited in a different manner without an adhesive; it is regularly cylindrical and rounded at each end, the micropylar end having short, recurved processes. *Nysius inconspicuus* has been captured on tea (*Thea sinensis* L.) and, according to Usinger, *Nysius pulchellus* Stål 1859, occurs most commonly on *Euphorbia hirta*, *Portulaca*, *Pemphis* and *Vernonia*. The ova are deposited somewhat loosely in composite heads.

Nysius caledoniæ Distant 1920, occurs on *Emelia*, a plant introduced into the island of Guam and it has also been collected on the closely related composite *Erigon* in the Philippine Islands.

Blissus leucopterus (Say) 1832 (**Blissinæ**), is an important pest of cultivated Gramineæ. Another species referred to by Usinger, *Pachybrachius nigriceps* (Dallas) 1852 (**Rhyparochrominæ**) was captured on *Tournefortia*, *Styphelia*, *Euphorbia hirta* and recorded as depositing ova on the top of flower heads among the small flowers of Heliotrope. They were placed crosswise and rather loosely in the open but were fastened together and to the flower calyx. They are elongate, slightly curved and about 1·00 mm. in length by 0·35 mm. in diameter. The micropylar end is thicker, sub-truncate and the opposite end tapered and rounded. The chorion is sculptured, exhibiting prominent hexagonal reticulations anteriorly. Near

---

Plate 2 (*facing*)
COREIDÆ
1. *Pachylis pharaonis* (Herbst) 1784.
2. *Petascelis remipes* Signoret 1847.
3. *Prionolomia malaya* Stål 1865.
4. *Acanthocephala latipes* Drury 1782.
5. *Plectrocnemia lobata* Haglund 1895.
6. *Derepteryx chinai* Miller 1931.
7. *Hormambogaster expansus* Karsch 1892.
8. *Spartocera pantomima* (Distant) 1901.
9. *Machtima mexicana* Stål 1870.
10. *Leptoglossus zonatus* Dallas 1852.
11. *Anisocelis flavolineata* Blanchard 1859.
12. *Petalops distinctus* Montandon 1895.
13. *Hypselopus annulicornis* Stål 1855.
14. *Holymenia histrio* (Fabricius) 1803.
15. *Pephricus livingstoni* Westwood 1857.
16. *Leptocorisa acuta* Thunberg 1783.
17. *Leptocoris rufomarginata* (Fabricius) 1794.
18. *Dulichius inflatus* Kirby 1891.
19. *Corizus latus* Jakowleff 1882.
Note: Nos. 1-15 Coreidæ-Coreinæ; 16 and 18 Alydinæ; 17 and 19 Rhopalinæ.

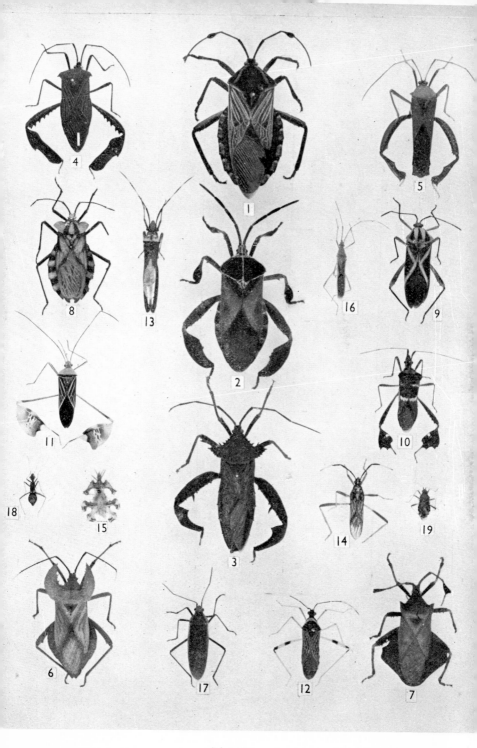

Plate II

the middle the reticulations become inconspicuous or appear as slight rugosities. The posterior end is perfectly smooth and the entire surface is shining white. There are five small but distinct processes forming a small ring at the micropylar end.

Aphanus litorralis has been recorded as feeding on freshly harvested stored groundnuts, on sesamum, *Carthemus tinctorius*, millet and on *Solanum nigrum*. It is not clear exactly in what manner the ova are deposited by the female, but it would seem, from the few observations made, that they are placed in loose groups in the soil, or in the case of those females attacking products in storehouses, among dust and rubbish on the floors.

Geocoris liolestes Hesse 1947 (**Geocorinæ**) has been recorded as a predator of the red scale of Citrus in South Africa.

Apart from those quoted, oviposition methods of Lygæidæ are known hardly at all, but it is not unlikely that some species insert their ova into plant tissues or in crevices in bark or other material.

Some species of *Oxycarenus* Fieber 1836 (**Oxycareninæ**) are pests of the cotton plant on the seeds of which they feed. Lygæidæ, however, are not exclusively phytophagous. For example, species of *Geocoris* Fallen 1814 have been reported as feeding on various plantbugs and I have found a species of *Dieuches* Dohrn 1860 (**Rhyparochrominæ**) feeding on the excreta of *Hyrax* sp. (Mammalia), and *Oncopeltus jucundus* Dallas 1852 (**Lygæinæ**) feeding on crushed millepedes in Southern Rhodesia.

A carnivorous diet is probable of some genera of the subfamily **Blissinæ** judging by the structure of the anterior legs in some species. For example, in *Spalacocoris sulcatus* Walker 1872 and in a species of *Chelochirus* Spinola 1839 they are strongly spined. The anterior tibiæ of the former have forwardly directed spines at the apex which suggests that they may be used for excavation purposes also.

Habitats of Lygæidæ include plants and under stones among leaf-debris. One myrmecophilous species has been described. This is *Neoblissus parasitaster* Bergroth 1903 (**Blissinæ**) which lives in the nests of *Solenopsis geminata* Fabricius in Brazil. It is reported to feed on the food stores of the ant. Some species have been attracted to artificial light which suggests nocturnal habits.

'Stink' glands are present in the neanides, so far as observation goes, and are situated on the third and fourth abdominal segments.

There are fifteen subfamilies: **Rhyparochrominæ** Stål 1862, **Geocorinæ** Stål 1862, **Blissinæ** Stål 1862, **Cyminæ** Stål 1862, **Lygæinæ** Stål 1862, **Oxycareninæ** Stål 1862, **Pamphantinæ** Barber and Bruner 1933, **Malcinæ** Stål 1865, **Chauliopinæ** Breddin 1907, **Lipostemmatinæ** Berg 1879, **Bledionotinæ** Reuter 1878, **Henes-**

tarinæ Douglas and Scott 1865, **Pachygronthinæ** Stål 1865, **Heterogastrinæ** Stål 1872, and **Artheneinæ** Stål 1872.

Rhyparochrominæ Stål 1862, have thick and frequently spined anterior femora.

Geocorinæ Stål 1862, in which the head is very wide, the hemelytra convex and punctate and the anterior femora normal.

Blissinæ Stål 1862, are mostly small or very small, somewhat narrow, elongate insects.

Cyminæ Stål 1862, are small with the head, pronotum, scutellum and hemelytra punctate and the internal veins of the membrane not connected at the base by a transverse vein.

Lygæinæ Stål 1862, contain some of the larger members of the family. They have the head, pronotum, scutellum and hemelytra usually impunctate and the two internal veins of the membrane generally joined at the base by a transverse vein.

Oxycareninæ Stål 1862, are small insects with the anterior femora moderately incrassate and armed with a spine. The corium is much wider than the abdomen.

Pamphantinæ Barber and Bruner 1933, are very small, narrow insects, with the head including the eyes wider than the pronotum. The head, pronotum, scutellum and corium are strongly punctate, the pronotum constricted beyond the middle and all the femora moderately thick.

Malcinæ Stål 1865, very small insects with relatively long antennæ, the basal and apical segments of which are thickened; head, pronotum, scutellum and corium strongly punctate; connexival segments produced and the veins of the membrane prominent; the internal veins form a distinct closed cell.

Chauliopinæ Breddin 1907, are allied to the Malcinæ and characterized by the spiracles being located on the dorsal side of the connexivum, and by the free and continuous veins of the membrane.

Lipostemmatinæ Berg 1879, very small oblong elliptical, somewhat depressed insects, densely pilose with a moderately wide head,

---

Fig. 9 (*facing*)
NEANIDES OF PLATASPIDÆ, PENTATOMIDÆ, COREIDÆ, PYRRHOCORIDÆ, PIESMIDÆ (*facing*)

1. *Chrysocoris stockerus* Linnæus 1764. Pentatomidæ-Scutellerinæ. 4th instar.
2. *Brachyplatys vahlii* (Fabricius) 1787. Plataspidæ. 1st instar.
3. *Eusthenes robustus* Lepeletier and Serville 1825. Pentatomidæ-
Tessaratominæ. 1st instar.
4. *Plataspis* sp. Plataspidæ. 4th instar.
5. *Antilochus nigripes* Burmeister 1835. Pyrrhocoridæ. 2nd instar.
6. *Physomerus parvulus* Dallas 1851. Coreidæ-Coreinæ. 1st instar.
7. *Piesma quadrata* Fieber 1861. Piesmidæ. 5th instar.
8. *Gonopsis pallescens* Distant 1902. Pentatomidæ-Phyllocephalinæ. 4th instar.
9. *Ectatops* sp. Pyrrhocoridæ. 4th instar.

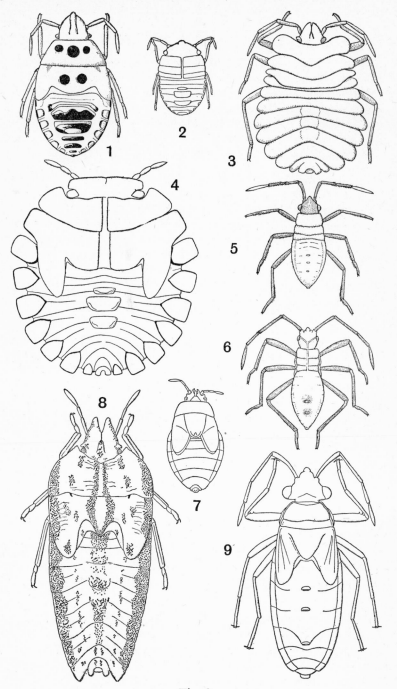

Fig. 9

which is feebly convex, narrowed posteriorly and obtusely acuminate; eyes large with large facets, ocelli absent, pronotum trapezoidal. Hemelytra complete with costa of corium feebly sinuate; legs normal, femora unarmed, membrane with three veins.

Bledionotinæ Reuter 1878, oblong in outline and remotely pilose; head triangular with the basal antennal segments extending a little beyond the apex of the tylus; all femora elongate, somewhat incrassate and unarmed; segments two to five of abdomen fused.

Henestarinæ Douglas and Scott 1865, small insects, oblong in outline with large pedunculate eyes; basal segments of antennæ thicker than remaining segments, extending beyond apex of head; all femora moderately incrassate, pronotum wide as long; head, body and corium remotely pilose.

Pachygronthinæ Stål 1865, small to moderately large elongate insects; antennæ with basal segment longer than head and pronotum together; anterior femora incrassate and with spines on lower surface; anterior tibia shorter than femur; basal segment of tarsi longer than remaining two segments together; vertex with a lateral carina.

Heterogastrinæ Stål 1872, small insects with the pronotum wider than long and with the lateral margins dorsoventrally compressed, straight and feebly constricted; anterior femora somewhat incrassate and sulcate on lower surface.

Artheneinæ Stål 1872, very small insects with the pronotum as long as wide, and with the lateral margins dorsoventrally compressed, straight; pronotum feebly constricted medially sub-laterally; basal antennal segment not extending to apex of head; scutellum with a deep depression; anterior femora moderately incrassate; anterior tibia shorter than femur.

References

Bergroth 1903; Corby 1947; Dahms and Kagan 1938; Hesse 1947; Kirkpatrick 1923; Lent 1939; Milliken and Wadley 1922; Poisson 1930; Slater 1951; Usinger 1942 a, 1946 a; York 1944.

PYRRHOCORIDAE Dohrn 1859 *Cat. Hem.* p. 36 (Plate 3)

On the whole, the Pyrrhocoridæ are larger and more robust insects, and on account of their brighter colours, are more conspicuous than the Lygæidæ. There are approximately four hundred known species and their distribution is world-wide.

The principal characters are: ocelli absent; antennæ with four segments; scutellum small, triangular; hemelytra usually complete with clavus, corium and membrane; tarsi with three segments.

Some species, namely *Melamphaus faber* (Fabricius) 1787 and several species of *Dysdercus* Amyot and Serville 1843, are of economic importance. *M. faber* has been recorded as damaging the seeds of *Hydnocarpus* in Malaya, and *Dysdercus* spp. are pests of the cotton plant.

Information concerning the ecology and developmental stages of Pyrrhocoridæ is very scanty, since only those damaging economic crops have been studied to any extent.

It would seem that the ova are deposited in large groups in soil and leaf-mould. They are ovate with the surface of the chorion smooth and shining. Eclosion is effected by the embryo splitting the chorion more or less along its longer axis. The adults and neanides in subtropical regions conceal themselves in leaf-debris and under logs or bark during the cold season.

Certain species of Dysdercus attack plants other than cotton. For example, *Dysdercus cingulatus* (Fabricius) 1775 has been reported as attacking bottle gourd (*Lagenaria vulgaris*), musk mallow (*Hibiscus abelmoschus*) and cabbage (*Brassica oleracea*).

The Pyrrhocoridæ appear to be mainly phytophagous, but among them, at least two carnivorous species have come to notice. They are *Dindymus rubiginosus* (Fabricius) 1787, a species resembling *Dysdercus* which attacks larvæ of *Oreta extensa* Walker (Lepidoptera-Drepanidæ) and adults of *Lawana candida* (Fabricius), (Homoptera-Flatidæ) and *Antilochus coqueberti* (Fabricius) 1803, killing *Dysdercus cingulatus*.

Most of the Pyrrhocoridæ are fully alate. There are, however, some apterous genera, namely, *Courtesius* Distant 1903 from India, and *Myrmoplata* Gerstaecker 1892 which occurs in the Ethiopian and Oriental Regions.

Brachyptery often occurs, e.g., in the genera *Scantius* Stål 1865, (Oriental and Ethiopian Regions), *Pyrrhocoris* Fallen 1814 (Palæarctic Region), *Cenæus* Stål 1861 and *Dermatinus* Stål 1853 (Ethiopian Region).

References
China 1954; Kirkaldy 1900; Miller 1932 a; Whitfield 1933.

LARGIDAE Dohrn 1859 *Cat. Hem.* p. 36 (Plate 3)

The Largidæ are separated from the Pyrrhocoridæ by having the seventh ventral segment of the female medially divided. Their habits are similar to those of the Pyrrhocoridæ, so far as is known.

The very large and sexually dimorphic *Lohita grandis* Gray 1832, is of some economic importance. *Euryopthalmus sellatus* (Guerin) 1857 is apparently carnivorous.

Two somewhat remarkable species, both from the point of view of colouration and structure, are *Astemma stylopthalma* Stål 1870, a black species with a bright red corium and pedunculate eyes, and *Fibrena gibbicollis* Stål 1861, in which the male has the anterior lobe of the pronotum gibbose. The female is of normal shape.

Brachyptery occurs in *Arhaphe* Herrich-Schaeffer 1853, *Japetus* Distant 1883, *Phæax* Distant 1893 and *Stenomacra* Stål 1870, all Neotropical, except *Arhaphe* which is distributed in the Palæarctic Region and in the Sonoran sub-region. It should be noted that the name *Japetus* is preoccupied. (Homoptera). *Lohita grandis* has been recorded from Burma, Cochin China and Sumatra.

So far as is known, oviposition methods are similar to those of the Pyrrhocoridæ. An ovipositor is present in *Euryopthalmus* which may indicate a different mode of oviposition. The Largidæ are probably more nearly related to the Lygæidæ than to the Pyrrhocoridæ.

PIESMIDAE Spinola 1850 Tav. Sinot. 44.

A family containing three genera only. It is characterized by having the scutellum exposed, ocelli, coriaceous hemelytra with distinct clavus corium and membrane. Most of the species–of which there are about twenty–are Palæarctic. There are also some species distributed in the Nearctic and Ethiopian Regions. The genus *Miespa* Drake 1948 has been recorded in Chile, and *Mcatella* Drake 1924, from Australia.

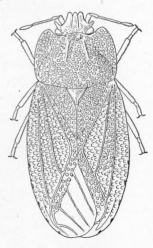

Fig. 10
Piesma diluta Stål 1855
(Piesmidæ)

A Palæarctic species *Piesma quadrata* Fieber 1861 has been extensively studied by Wille. Its ova which are about 0·60 mm. in length are usually deposited with the longer axis parallel to the substratum. An operculum such as is found in the ovum of *Cimex lectularius* Linnæus 1758 (Cimicidæ-Cimicinæ) is present and is provided with five or six processes for the purpose of aeration.

The operculum, however, on eclosion of the neanide splits in five or six directions and is not removed entire by the emerging embryo, of which the cuticle enveloping it remains attached to the chorion.

Piesma quadrata is an important pest of beet.

Stridulation has been reported

to occur in this species. This is dealt with in the chapter on this subject.

Dorsal abdominal glands are present on the fourth and fifth segments.

References

Leston 1954 a; Wille 1929.

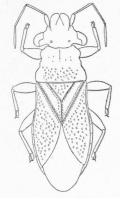

Fig. 11

Thaumastocoris australicus Kirkaldy 1908.
(Thaumastocoridæ)

THAUMASTOCORIDAE Kirkaldy 1908, *Proc. Linn. Soc. N.S.W.* **32**, 789.

Representatives of this family are small with an elongate body and wide head. The eyes and ocelli are large, the former pedunculate; the rostrum and scutellum short. The hemelytra which are as long or longer than the abdomen in macropterous forms have a distinct clavus, corium and membrane but no nervures. The tibiæ have a membranous process almost as long as the tarsi, apically.

The Thaumastocoridæ are distributed in the Australian and Nearctic Regions.

There is, so far as I know, no information on the ecology of the family.

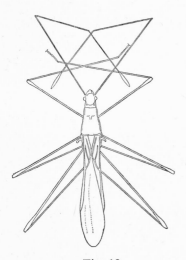

Fig. 12

Metacanthus pertenerum Breddin 1907
(Berytidæ)

BERYTIDAE Fieber 1860 *Genera Hydroc.* 9

Small, delicate insects with an elongate linear body and long slender legs, the femora of which are thickened apically. The basal and apical antennal segments are also thickened apically. The peritreme of the metathoracic gland ostioles is produced.

About one hundred species are known; these are distributed in the Ethiopian and Indo-Australian Regions and belong to two subfamilies, the **Berytinæ** Puton 1886 and **Metacanthinæ** Douglas and Scott 1865. The **Berytinæ** have an elongate head with the vertex produced above the tylus; the

Metacanthinæ have a shorter head and no process on the vertex. The Berytidæ are found mainly among grasses and on tree-trunks. *Gampsocoris pulchellus* (Dallas) 1852 (**Metacanthinæ**) in both the neanide and adult stages has been recorded on cacao, the young shoots of which they attack. The female deposits its ova singly among the shoots. The ovum is whitish, cylindrical, somewhat curved and rounded at each end and with the surface striate.

This species has also been found on *Hibiscus mutabilis* and *Passiflora foetida*. Adults have been seen to be attacked by adults of *Cosmolestes picticeps* Stål 1859 (Reduviidæ-Harpactorinæ).

The ovum of *Metatropis rufescens* Herrich-Schaeffer 1835 (**Metacanthinæ**) is cylindrical tapering posteriorly and with four minute button-shaped processes or tubercles at the anterior end. It may be attached to the substratum by a small stout support or stalk, but not in all cases.

On eclosion the neanide causes the chorion to split longitudinally at the anterior end. In relation to the size of the adult the ovum is very small.

References
Massee 1949, Miller 1941.

COLOBATHRISTIDAE Stål 1865, *Hem. Afr.* **2**, 121

Slender elongate Heteroptera with the head almost vertical, long and slender antennæ, a sculptured thorax and scutellum bearing spines or tubercles, long legs, large eyes and ocelli. Brachypterous forms occur in the genus *Trichocentrus* Horvath 1904.

About seventy species are known. These are distributed in the Neotropical and Indo-Australian Regions. Very little is known about their ecology.

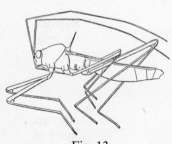

Fig. 13
Phænacantha suturalis Horvath 1904.
(Colobathristidæ)

The ovum of a species of *Phænacantha* Horvath 1904 from Borneo is cylindrical with ten or more short, chorionic processes and some short tubercles on the chorion. This information is based on fragments of a dissected ovum.

Phænacantha saccaricida (Karsch) 1888 is a pest of sugar cane in Java. The adults and neanides feed on the undersides of the cane leaves. Ova are deposited mostly in damp places, singly and close to or in the soil.

References
van Deventer 1906; Kalshoven 1950.

ARADIDAE Amyot and Serville 1843, *Hém.* 306

Members of the family Aradidæ are all of dull colouration and some of them are brachypterous. Although the alate forms are relatively active and sometimes, during flight, are attracted to artificial light, in the main they are photophobic and pass most of their existence in concealment, often under the loose bark of decaying trees. They are also found on foliage.

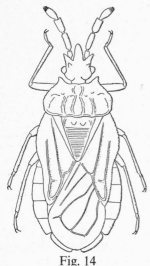

Their food appears to be mainly fungi, the mycelia of which are usually abundant in decaying timber. To be able to follow the ramifications of the mycelia the stylets of the Aradidæ are admirably suited, being very long. The rostrum, on the other hand, is usually relatively short. When the stylets are not in use they are coiled in the anterior part of the head.

Not a great deal is known about the ecology of the Aradidæ. Ova are usually deposited under bark. The ovum of *Aradus depressus* (Fabricius) 1803 is oval, white with a faint greenish tinge; there is a ring of low elevations at the anterior end. The embryo ruptures the chorion within this ring. The ova are attached by the side and are deposited singly. Scent glands are present in most species.

Fig. 14
Aradus depressus (Fabricius) 1803
(Aradidæ)

The Aradidæ are distributed in the Palæarctic and Nearctic Regions.

References

Barber 1923; Bueno, de la Torre 1935; Butler 1923; Jordan 1932; Kiritschenko 1913

MEZIRIDAE Oshanin 1908 *Verz. Paläark. Hem.* 478. (Plate 3)

Dull-coloured, flattened insects which live under bark of dead trees and feed on the mycelia of fungi. They closely resemble the Aradidæ in many respects as regards habitus and mode of life; they differ mainly in having the head widened behind the eyes and a very short rostrum which rests in a sulcus on the lower surface of the head when not in use. The stylets are very long, in some species longer than the head and body together.

There are many apterous species, among which may be mentioned *Chelonocoris* Miller 1938, *Chelysocoris* Miller 1949, *Emydocoris* Usinger 1941, *Notoplocoris* Usinger 1941 and *Chelonoderus* Drake 1942.

An interesting feature of some of the apterous genera is the thick tomentose clothing or a tenuous covering of a resin-like substance, both of which conceal to a marked degree the actual habitus and also the somewhat complicated sculpturation which adorns the dorsal surface of the thorax and abdomen.

So far as is known, most of the Meziridæ have mainly subcorticolous habits but they do not spend all their existence in such a habitat, at least as regards the alate forms which are often attracted to artificial light.

The neanides of some species, for example, *Mezira membranacea* (Fabricius) 1803 remain congregated together under bark during their entire developmental stage.

The Meziridæ are mainly tropicopolitan in distribution. There are two subfamilies: **Mezirinæ** Oshanin 1908, with the rostrum not extending beyond the base of the head, the prosternum not sulcate, the head wider behind the eyes than in front, spiracles equidistant between basal and apical margins of segments; and **Isoderminæ** Stål 1872, which are strongly dorso-ventrally compressed and have the anteocular produced, the postocular widened immediately behind the eyes, the rostrum much shorter than the head, the hemelytra not covering the entire dorsal surface of the abdomen, the femora spined on the lower surface and the tarsi with two segments. They are distributed only in the extreme south of South America and in the Australian sub-region.

References

Miller 1938; Usinger 1941, 1950; Wygodzinsky 1946 b.

ANEURIDAE Douglas and Scott *Brit. Hem.* 26 and 267

The Aneuridæ are very small, flattened insects with the head and pronotum transverse, the former with a distinct neck. The rostrum is very short and composed of three segments. The scutellum is large and semi-circular. Hemelytra with corium and membrane not differentiated; veins of corium indistinct. Abdomen much wider than hemelytra; connexivum wide.

The Aneuridæ live under the bark of dead trees and their food is probably the mycelia of fungi. They are distributed in all zoogeographical regions.

TERMITAPHIDIDAE Myers *Psyche* Camb., Mass., **31**, 6, 267

The Termitaphididæ are very small insects, elliptical in outline without eyes or ocelli and with the lateral margins of the thorax laminate, the external margin of each lamella having tubercles and flagella.

Apart from a few details regarding the ova of *Termitaradus trinidadensis* (Morrison) 1923 and of *T. guianæ* (Morrison) 1923 little is known about the ecology of these small and obscurely coloured insects.

Fig. 15

Aneurus lævis (Fabricius) 1803 (Aneuridæ)

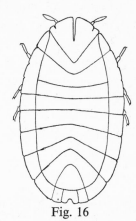

Fig. 16

Termitaradus panamensis Myers 1924. (Termitaphididæ)

In 1902 a curious termitophilous insect was discovered and, at the time, was considered to be an abnormal aphid. For this insect, Wasmann erected the genus *Termitaphis*, but, nine years later, Silvestri, when describing two more new species, came to the conclusion that the genus did not belong to the Homoptera. He therefore placed it in the Heteroptera and established a new family, the Termitocoridæ, to receive it. On account of the fact, however, that a family name must be derived from the type genus (the genus *Termitocoris* being non-existent) the name of the family must be Termitaphididæ.

The species known up to the present, ten in all, have been found in the nests of termites but it has not been definitely established what their food is.

An examination of the stylets has revealed a resemblance to those of the Aradidæ for they are very long and spirally coiled in the head capsule. It is assumed, as in the Aradidæ, that these elongate mouth-parts are adapted for feeding on the mycelia of fungi. On the other hand, it is not improbable that the Termitaphididæ may be carnivorous and with their long stylets may be able to reach such insects as coleopterous larvæ feeding below the surface.

The ova of *Termitardus guianæ* are described as follows: The surface is smooth, extremely polished and porcelain-like. Under very strong direct light it is possible to discern a faint and somewhat irregular pitting. There is not the slightest external sign of micropylar apparatus or cap; nor does there appear any difference in the evanescent pitting in different parts of the chorion.

The dimensions of the ova, which are ovoid, are 0·86 mm. × 0·56 mm.

Termitaphididæ have been recorded from Central America, the West Indies, India and Africa.

References

Mjöberg 1914; Morrison 1923; Myers 1924, 1932; Silvestri 1911, 1921; Usinger 1942 b.

JOPPEICIDAE Reuter 1910 *Acta. Soc. Sci. fenn.* **37,** 3, 75.

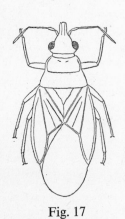

Fig. 17

Joppeicus paradoxus Puton 1898. (Joppeicidæ)

Small insects with the rostrum, which is composed of four segments, directed forwards, short legs and tarsi with two segments. The hemelytra have a strongly sclerotized corium and large membrane with four nervures. They are related, according to China, to the Reduviidæ.

There is one genus, *Joppeicus* Puton 1881, found in Syria, but very little is known about it. It occurs on *Ficus sycomorus* where, no doubt, it lives as a predator on other small insects.

Neanidal *Joppeicus* have three abdominal glands. The segmentation of the abdomen being abnormal, however, the ostioles are on the fourth, fifth and seventh segments towards the anterior margin but separated from it.

Reference

China 1955 a.

TINGIDAE Laporte 1832, *Essai Classif. Syst. Hem.* 47

Mostly very small insects including several genera with striking modifications to the pronotum and hemelytra, the former concealing the scutellum. The hemelytra have neither corium nor membrane and are entirely areolate. Several species are of economic importance, occasionally causing defoliation.

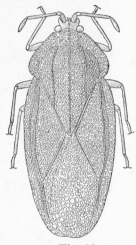

On the whole, little is known about the ecology of the Tingidæ. Ova have been found on leaves, usually the underside, and sometimes inserted into the tissue or with a covering of sticky substance.

The family is divided into three subfamilies: **Cantacaderinae** Stål 1873; **Agramminæ** Douglas and Scott 1865; and **Tinginæ** Douglas and Scott 1865.

Cantacaderinæ Stål have the head produced in front of the insertion of the antennæ and the bucculæ produced anteriorly.

Agramminæ Douglas and Scott with the head not produced in front of the insertion of the antennæ and the bucculæ not produced anteriorly; the pronotum has no hood and in the hemelytra the discal areas are absent or feebly defined; the lateral margins are not – or only feebly – dilated.

Fig. 18

Tingis cardui Linnæus 1785.
(Tingidæ)

Tinginæ Douglas and Scott. The largest division of the Tingidæ, in which there is an anterior hood which, in some cases, completely covers the head; the hemelytral areas are well-defined with the costal area frequently dilated.

References

Butler 1923; Leston 1954 b.

ENICOCEPHALIDAE Stål 1860 *Rio Jan. Hem.* **1,** 81

The Enicocephalidæ are characterized by the elongate head which is globose behind the eyes, by the somewhat elongate habitus and the entirely membranous hemelytra. Ocelli are present except in apterous genera. The structure of the rostrum is primitive and in the genus *Aenictopechys* Breddin 1905 it is extended forwards and not folded beneath the head. A stridulatory furrow is absent. Odoriferous glands present.

Fig. 19

Embolorrhinus cornifrons Bergroth 1905. (Enicocephalidæ)

Although the Enicocephalidæ are predaceous they are not provided with anterior legs of the true raptorial type, the anterior tibiæ being somewhat thick, and the tarsi are composed of one segment bearing one or two claws (mostly two) which are long in some genera.

This is one of the smaller families of the Heteroptera, and contains mostly small, obscurely coloured insects, the habits of which are imperfectly known. They are discovered, as a rule, in the process of sifting leaf and other debris. Some species have been observed to swarm and to fly in the sunshine after the manner of certain Diptera.

With regard to the predaceous habits of these insects, it is probable that within certain limits they are general feeders; but there is, however, a record which reveals that at least one species has a restricted diet, being myrmecophagous. This species is *Henicocephalus braunsi* Bergroth 1903, a South African species found in the nest of the ant *Rhoptromyrmex transversinodes* Mayr in Cape Colony. The opinion expressed by Bergroth that this Enicocephalid is myrmecophagous was based on the fact of its considerably larger size in relation to the ant.

Hardly any information exists regarding the developmental stages. The ovum of a species of *Enicocephalus* Westwood 1837 (*Henicocephalus*) from New Zealand has been described by Myers. This ovum is elliptical with parallel sides and rounded ends. In this instance, it was affixed by the female by one side to a rootlet.

The Enicocephalidæ are cosmopolitan and are found on all the principal continents and major groups of islands.

References

Bergroth 1903; Carayon 1950 a; Jeannel 1941; Myers 1926; Usinger 1932.

PHYMATIDAE Laporte 1832, *Essai Classif. Syst. Hém.* 14

Most of the Phymatidæ are small, frequently attractively coloured insects possessing raptorial anterior legs and having the pronotum and abdomen in some species laterally expanded. There are three subfamilies: **Macrocephalinæ** Dohrn 1859, **Carcinocorinæ** Handlirsch

1897 and **Phymatinæ** Dohrn 1859, in which apparently two types of anterior legs are represented. In the **Macrocephalinæ** the anterior tibia is curved and constitutes one arm of a pincers with the femur. The tarsus is sometimes lacking but when present can be lodged in a sulcus on the outer surface of the tibia when not in use. In the **Carcinocorinæ** the tibia is more or less straight and forms one arm of a pincers with the produced lower margin of the femur. In this type of anterior leg there is no tarsus.

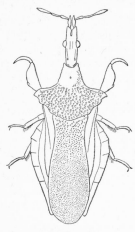

Fig. 20

Glossopelta montandoni Handlirsch 1897. (Phymatidæ)

The tibia of the **Macrocephalinæ** have a row of pegs on the inner surface and the femora two parallel rows or one irregular row; when these two parts of the leg are drawn together the pegs on the tibia fit between the rows of pegs on the femur.

The scutellum in **Macrocephalinæ** is very strongly produced. A tarsus is lacking from the anterior tibiæ of *Agreuocoris* Handlirsch 1897, *Glossopelta* Handlirsch 1897, *Narina* Distant 1906, *Carcinocoris* Handlirsch 1897, *Chelocoris* Bianchi 1899 and *Carcinochelis* Fieber 1861, but is present in *Phymata* Latreille 1802.

A stridulatory furrow is present in *Glossopelta, Agreuocoris, Amblythyreus* Westwood 1841, *Macrocephalus* Swederus 1787 and possibly *Narina* (**Macrocephalinæ**), *Carcinocoris, Carcinochelis* (**Carcinocorinæ**) and *Phymata* (**Phymatinæ**).

All species are predators but in prolonged absence of animal food on account of unfavourable conditions, they possibly have recourse to nectar or sap until their usual food is once more available.

The habits of Phymatidæ, all of which are diurnal, are the same as those of the Reduviidæ and they frequent flowers on which they wait for prey.

In the choice of a flower on which to take up a position a Phymatid (it would appear) is not influenced by its colour but by its attractiveness to other insects. It is clear, therefore, that it does not necessarily choose for the purposes of concealment a flower the colour of which harmonizes as closely as possible with its own body colour.

Unfortunately, there is little information regarding the habits and ecology of the Phymatidæ with the exception of that concerning

Phymata pennsylvanica americana Melin 1931 (**Phymatinæ**), the life history and habits of which have been extensively studied by Balduf.

This investigator in discussing the prey of Phymatidæ arrived at the conclusion that the range in size of the Arthropoda captured by them is very great, those recorded by him including the small and weak Mycetophilidæ, Anthocoridæ and Miridæ and large and robust Lepidoptera of the families Pieridæ and Noctuidæ.

Balduf states that the ova of *P. pennsylvanica americana* are deposited in masses of irregular shape containing variable numbers. Each ovum is more or less deeply embedded in a layer of frothy substance.

The ovum of *Macrocephalus notatus* Westwood 1841, according to Wygodzinsky, is ovate with the surface which is in contact with the substratum smooth. The female deposits them singly or in small groups without applying a glutinous substance to the exposed surface.

Readio has described and figured the ova of *Phymata erosa* Linnæus 1758 sub-sp. *fasciata* (Gray) 1832. They, like those of *pennsylvanica* are deposited in masses embedded individually in a frothy substance which leaves only the operculum and a portion of the chorion exposed. The female attached the mass to plant stems. The ovum is ovate with the opercular end oblique.

Fig. 21. Ova of Phymatidæ, Reduviidæ (*facing*)

1. *Phymata erosa* sub. *sp. fasciata* Gray 1832. Phymatidæ-Phymatinæ (after Readio).
2. *Stenolæmus marshalli* Distant 1903. 1·00 mm. Reduviidæ-Emesinæ.
3. *Polytoxus* sp. Red-Saicinæ.
4. *Ptilocnemus lemur* Westwood 1840. 1·60 mm. Red-Holoptilinæ.
5. *Stenopoda* sp. 2·80 mm. Red-Stenopodinæ.
6. *Canthesancus gulo* Stål 1863. 2·20 mm. Red-Stenopodinæ.
7. *Pygolampis* sp. 1·30 mm. Red-Stenopodinæ.
8. *Oncocephalus* sp. 1·20 mm. Red-Stenopodinæ.
9. *Elaphocranum* sp. 1·30 mm. Red-Salyavatinæ.
10. *Lisarda* sp. ·80 mm. Red-Salyavatinæ.
11. *Salyavata variegata* Amyot and Serville 1843. 2·10 mm. Red-Salyavatinæ (after Wygodzinsky).
12. *Petalochirus brachialis* Stål 1858. 1·00 mm. Red-Salyavatinæ.
13. *Alvilla* sp. ·80 mm. Red-Salyavatinæ.
14. *Petalochirus obesus* Miller 1940. 1·00 mm. Red-Salyavatinæ.
15. *Inara alboguttata* Stål 1863. 1·90 mm. Red-Reduviinæ.
16. *Centraspis imperialis* Westwood 1845. 3·50 mm. Red-Ectrichodiinæ.
17. *Platymerus* sp. 4·00 mm. Red-Reduviinæ.
18. *Psyttala horrida* Stål 1865. 3·50 mm. Red-Reduviinæ.
19. *Inara iracunda* Miller 1940. 2·00 mm. Red-Reduviinæ.
20. *Cerilocus dohrni* Stål 1858. 2·60 mm. Red-Reduviinæ.
21. *Pasiropsis vidua* Miller 1954. 1·80 mm. Red-Reduviinæ.
22. *Archilestidium cinnabarinum* China 1925. 1·20 mm. Red-Reduviinæ.
23. *Carcinomma simile* Horvath 1914. 1·00 mm. Red-Cetherinæ.
24. *Sphedanocoris sabulosus* Stål 1833. 1·20 mm. Red-Reduviinæ.
25. *Cheronea* sp. 1·30 mm. Red-Reduviinæ.

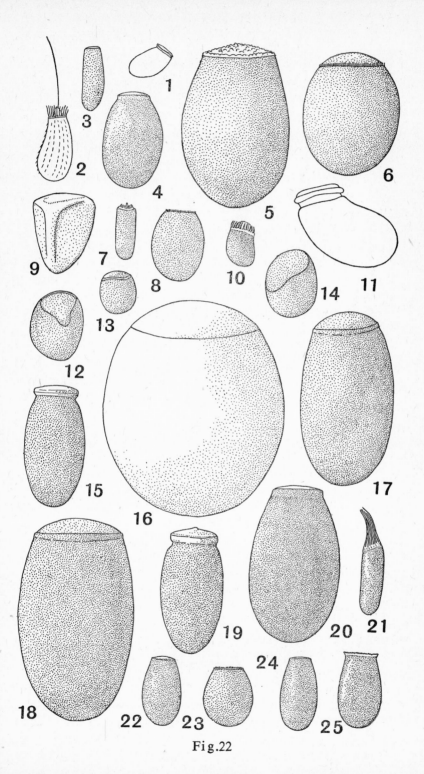

Fig.22

Phymatid ova exhibit some similarity to Reduviid ova in having similar chorial processes on the inner side of the rim of the chorion. The methods are similar, but, so far, no one has yet shown whether in the removal of the operculum the embryo is assisted by a specialized structure as may be seen on the embryonic cuticle of Reduviidæ.

The Phymatidæ are represented in all zoogeographical regions. The most widely distributed is *Phymata erosa* which occurs in both the Nearctic and Neotropical Regions.

References

Balduf 1939, 1941; Cook 1897; Readio 1927; Wygodzinsky 1944.

ELASMODEMIDAE Letheirry and Severin 1896, *Cat. Hém.* **3**, 49

Very small and strongly dorso-compressed insects with the head transverse divided by an arcuate transverse impression behind the eyes. The ocelli are distinct and located near the lateral margin of the postocular and adjacent to the eyes. The rostrum is very short, broad and curved. The pronotum is transversely impressed near the middle and the pro- and metathoracic acetabula project and are visible from above. The scutellum is short, wide and unarmed. The sterna are entirely flattened with a wide continuous plate-like surface and the coxæ are very widely separated. A short stridulatory furrow is present. The anterior legs are not of the raptorial type and the tibiæ are simple. The hemelytra have simple venation with R+M unbranched in the corium, Cu simple and unbranched and

the membrane with three simple veins which do not form cells and do not reach the apical margin. The vestiges of the neanidal abdominal gland are to be seen on the fourth segment.

Elasmodema erichsoni Stål 1860 has been found in Brazil living under the loose bark of fencing posts. *E. setigerum* (Usinger) 1943 has been recorded from Paraguay and Brasil and was discovered in a bird's nest along with other Arthropods. In the habitat of *E. erichsoni* a number of pseudoscorpions, Hemiptera of the families Aradidæ and Anthocoridæ, also Dermaptera, Coleoptera, dipterous larvæ, but chiefly Psocidæ was present.

Fig. 22

Elasmodema erichsoni Stål 1860. (Elasmodemidæ)

Another species *E. bosqui* Kormilev 1948 has been found in the Argentine. *Elas-*

modema species have strong thigmotactic tendencies but they are not markedly photophobic.

The ova of *E. erichsoni* are deposited by the female in irregular groups or singly and are always fixed to the timber and not to the internal face of the bark enclosing it.

The ovum is cylindrical. The chorion is finely sculptured with pentagons and hexagons. The number of ova deposited by a single female is unknown, but in view of its relatively large size – 1·50 mm. – and the size of the female, it is likely that very few ova develop at one time.

References

Kormilev 1948; Usinger 1943; Wygodzinsky 1944.

REDUVIIDAE Latreille 1807, *Gen. Crust. Ins.* 3, 126

(*Plates* 3 *and* 4)

The Reduviidæ form one of the largest families of the Heteroptera. So far as is known, all are exclusively predaceous. Representatives of the **Triatominæ** feed on mammalian and avian blood. Some of them are vectors of human trypanosomiasis. The family has the following characters: body more or less elongate, sometimes bacilliform or linear; head usually with a transverse sulcus behind or between the eyes; ocelli present, except sometimes in apterous forms; antennæ with four to eight segments; exceptionally with as many as forty segments; no genus with five segments; intercalary segments sometimes present in antennæ composed of four segments; stridulatory furrow generally present; rostrum nearly always composed of four segments; anterior and median tibiæ often with a *fossula spongiosa*; alary polymorphism frequent.

Apart from the hæmatophagous species, Reduviidæ are not of direct importance economically. Being mostly general feeders they are not effective in causing an appreciable reduction in the numbers of insect pests of crops. The Reduviidæ are to be found in many kinds of terrestrial habitat and are most abundant in tropical and subtropical regions. Some are found occasionally in caves, but there are no true cavernicolous Reduviidæ in the strict sense.

As to their habits they may, with reasonable accuracy, be divided into two categories, namely, diurnal and nocturnal. These two categories, however, are not always sharply defined. Diurnal species are found mainly on bushes, low herbage and sometimes fairly high up on the foliage. Nocturnal species remain in seclusion during the daytime, but occasionally may be seen in the open. Their appearance may be voluntary, for example, during the search for females or may have been caused by enemies, such as predatory ants, driving them from their hiding places.

Artificial light has a great attraction for both sexes of some nocturnal species. Females seem to be attracted less frequently and, it appears, only before or after oviposition, and not during the period of development of the ova. Diurnal species have occasionally been attracted to light, but this happens as a rule when the light shines on the plant on which they are resting.

Reduviidæ kill their prey by injecting saliva at the time of piercing the body of the victim with their stylets. The saliva has an almost instantaneous paralizing effect, except in the case of large Arthropods such as millipedes which are more resistant. Scent glands are present in most Reduviidæ. In the adult the ostioles of these glands are located in the metasternal depression and close to the rim of the posterior acetabulum. In certain genera there are two pairs of glands, the first pair in the position just mentioned and the other pair laterally near the posterior margin of the metapleural epimeron.

The position and number of the ostioles of the dorsal abdominal glands in the neanides varies, there being usually a pair each on segments three to six or only one pair on segment five (*Toxopeusiana* Miller 1954). Several genera are provided with glandular setæ through which a glutinous substance is secreted. These setæ are mostly on the body and legs.

The Reduviidæ are divided into twenty-nine subfamilies: **Holoptilinæ** Stål 1859, **Emesinæ** Spinola 1850, **Saicinæ** Stål 1859, **Visayanocorinæ** Miller 1952, **Tribelocephalinæ** Stål 1865, **Bactrodinæ** Stål 1865, **Stenopodinæ** Stål 1859, **Salyavatinæ** Stål 1859, **Eupheninæ** Miller 1955, **Cetherinæ** Jeannel 1919, **Sphæridopinæ** Costa Lima 1940, **Manangocorinæ** Miller 1954, **Physoderinæ** Miller 1954,

---

Plate 3 (*facing*)

Coreidæ, Lygæidæ, Pyrrhocoridæ, Meziridæ, Reduviidæ

1. *Lygæus elegans* Wolff 1802. Lygæidæ-Lygæinæ.
2. *Microspitus proximus* Dallas 1852. Lygæidæ-Lygæinæ.
3. *Stenocephala agilis* Scopoli 1763. Coreidæ-Alydinæ.
4. *Cænocoris floridulus* Distant 1918. Lygæidæ-Lygæinæ.
5. *Narbo fasciatus* Distant 1901. Lygæidæ-Rhyparochrominæ.
6. *Bedunia intermedia* (Distant) 1882. Lygæidæ-Rhyparochrominæ.
7. *Lohita grandis* (Gray) 1832. Largidæ.
8. *Euryopthalmus subligatus* Distant 1882. Largidæ.
9. *Melamphaus faber* (Fabricius) 1782. Pyrrhocoridæ.
10. *Mezira membranacea* (Fabricius) 1803. Meziridæ.
11. *Dysodius lunatus* (Fabricius) 1794. Meziridæ.
12. *Bagauda lucifugus* McAtee and Malloch 1926. Reduviidæ-Emesinæ.
13. *Polytoxus pallescens* Distant 1903. Reduviidæ-Saicinæ.
14. *Tribelocephala* sp. Reduviidæ-Tribelocephalinæ.
15. *Sminthus fuscipennis* Stål 1874. Reduviidæ-Reduviinæ.
16. *Tiarodes cruentus* Stål 1870. Reduviidæ-Reduviinæ.

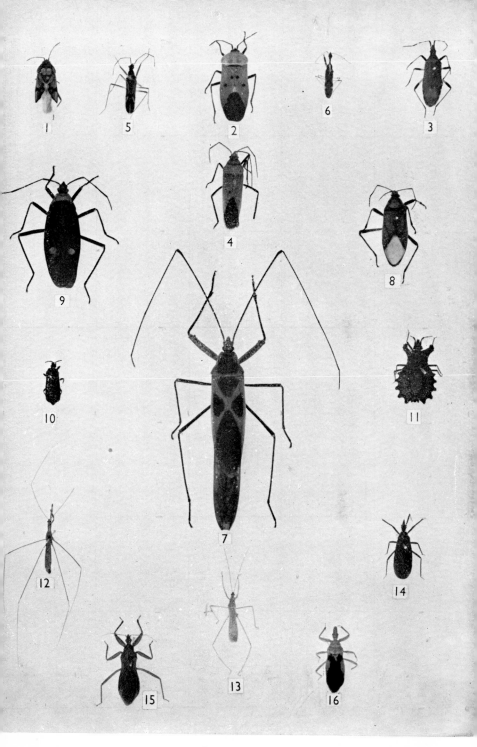

Plate III

Chryxinæ Champion 1898, Vesciinæ Fracker and Bruner 1924, Reduviinæ Spinola 1850, Triatominæ Jannel 1919, Piratinæ Stål 1859, Phimophorinæ Handlirsch 1897, Pachynominæ Stål 1873, Hammacerinæ Stål 1859, Ectrichodinæ Spinola 1850, Perissoryhnchinæ Miller 1952, Rhaphidosominæ Jannel 1919, Harpactorinæ Spinola 1850 Apiomerinæ Stål 1859, Ectinoderinæ Stål 1866, Phonolibinæ Miller 1952 and Tegeinæ Villiers 1948.

Holoptilinæ Stål 1859, are characterized by the ample, almost entirely membranous hemelytra, by the transverse head, dilated pronotum and by the abundant long setæ on the antennæ and posterior tibiæ. It is also noteworthy that the setæ are of various types, simple, serrate or pinnate.

In colour, the Holoptilinæ are mainly light brown with darker brown or piceous spots and suffusion on the hemelytra, or, in *Ptilocnemus* Westwood 1840, for example, the hemelytra are hyaline with dark brown spots. Although frequently seen on the wing, their flight being moth-like, they are more often found in shady places on branches or among leaves. The metathoracic wings are usually much reduced.

Information regarding the habits of the Holoptilinæ is scanty, consisting almost solely of observations on *Ptilocerus ochraceus* Montandon 1907 by Jacobson, who relates how he found this insect in very large numbers, adults as well as neanides, in company with numerous small black ants, *Dolichoderus bituberculatus* Mayr, a soft-bodied species.

Jacobson suggested that this ant is particularly fond of sweet substances, and went on to state that 'most of the ants which I found in the above-named locality near the bugs appeared to be in a more or less paralized state, and the ground beneath was in some places covered an inch thick with dead ants'. Later on he was able to observe the behaviour of this Reduviid, some of which he caged with the ants. 'The bugs', he stated, 'had fasted for about a week, the only thing I had given them being pure water sprinkled in their cage and which they readily absorbed. They were, however, none the worse for the fasting, only a few of the many hundreds I had captured having died'.

Ptilocerus Gray 1831 and other genera of this subfamily possess what is termed a trichome. This is formed by a strong elevation or gibbosity on the third ventral segment of the abdomen which, incidentally, is fused with the second segment. This elevation is surmounted and flanked by a dense tuft of setæ and on its anterior surface is situated the ostiole of a gland which extends posteriorly along the wall of the abdomen to the fifth segment in *Ptilocnemus lemur* Westwood 1840. From the gland a substance agreeable to ants is said to be excreted and it is also considered to have intoxicating properties.

Jacobson described how a bug, on the approach of an ant, raised itself on its legs so that the trichome was exposed. The ant then licked the trichome and pulled the tuft of setæ with its mandibles, but it was not until the fluid from it began to take effect that the bug inserted its mouthparts into a soft part of the ant's body. To support his statement that the fluid has paralizing or intoxicating properties, Jacobson said that sometimes the ants licked the trichome and left without being seized by a bug. Soon after, however, they were affected and thus many more ants died as a result of imbibing the fluid and not by direct attack by *Ptilocerus*.

Since these Reduviidæ, like others of the family, inject their saliva – which is very potent – into the body of the victim, the possession of a subsidiary method for overcoming it, seems superfluous. Much fuller investigation is desirable before the behaviour of *Ptilocerus* as described is confirmed beyond all reasonable doubt.

Jacobson also stated that the 'nymphs and adults of the bug act in exactly the same manner to lure the ants to their destruction after having rendered them helpless by treating them to a tempting delicacy'.

Fig. 23   Ova of Reduviidæ (*facing*)

1. *Centrocnemis signoreti* Stål 1863. 3·00 mm.
2. *Psophis consanguinea* Distant 1903. 2·50 mm.
3. *Dyakocoris vulnerans* (Stål) 1863. 2·20 mm.
4. *Zelurus luteoguttatus* (Stål) 1854. 2·00 mm.
5. *Sminthus* sp. 2·50 mm.
6. *Drescherocoris horridus* Miller 1954. 1·20 mm.
7. *Holotrichius tenebrosus* Burmeister 1835. 1·50 mm.
8. *Velitra alboplagiata* (Stål) 1859. 2·10 mm.
9. *Zelurus limbatus* (Lepeletier and Serville) 1825. 1·50 mm.
10. *Durganda rubra* Amyot and Serville 1843. 1·30 mm.
11. *Acanthaspis* sp. 1·80 mm.
12. *Phyja tricolor* Distant 1919. 2·30 mm.
13. *Cethera musiva* (Germar) 1837. 0·90 mm.
14. *Acanthaspis fulvipes* Dallas 1850. 2·00 mm.
15. *Physoderes patagiata* Miller 1941. 1·00 mm.
16. *Kopsteinia variegata* Miller 1954. 1·00 mm.
17. *Velitra rubropicta* Amyot and Serville 1843. 2·00 mm.
18. *Neostachyogenys tristis* Miller 1953. 1·40 mm.
19. *Acanthaspis flavovaria* Hahn 1834. 1·50 mm.
20. *Eupheno* sp. Eupheninæ. 1·40 mm.
21. *Tiarodes nigrirostris* Stål 1859. 2·60 mm.
22. *Catamiarus nyassæ* Distant 1877. 3·20 mm. Piratinæ.
23. *Ectomocoris fenestratus* Horvath 1911. 3·10 mm. Piratinæ.
24. *Rasahus sulcicollis* Serville 1831. 2·80 mm. Piratinæ.
(*Note*: No. 1- 19 and 21 all Reduviinæ except No. 13 Cetherinæ and No. 15 Physoderinæ).

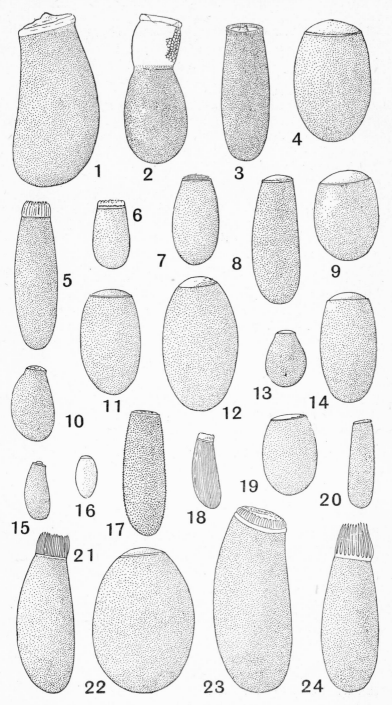

Fig. 23

In the fourth instar neanide of *Ptilocerus ochraceus* there is a certain degree of gibbosity on the third abdominal segment, but whether this has an ostiole connected to a functional gland can be determined only by dissection of fresh specimens. Dorsal abdominal glands are present in neanides of *P. ochraceus*, the ostioles of which are situated on the fourth and fifth segments. In *Montandoniola* Villiers 1946 there is no visible trichome in the adults.

The ova of *P. ochraceus* are deposited in irregular groups in concealed places, *e.g.*, on the inner surface of a bamboo, and are more or less covered with a white exudation. According to Kirkaldy the ovum is 'obtusely flask-shaped, flattened down ventrally; the lid is provided with a small knob. Colour brown; chorion well chitinized with finely reticulated surface composed of hexagonal and pentagonal areas. Size 1·2 x 0·5 mm.'. An ovum of *P. lemur* dissected from a dried specimen was dark brown in colour with a whitish operculum, and ovate, constricted at the upper margin of the chorion which was glabrous. The size – 1·60 mm. In view of the small size of the adult, this is a large ovum. Probably only six to eight develop at one time. No trichome appears to be present in the neanides of *P. lemur*.

Emesinæ Spinola 1850, are small or moderately large, slender fragile insects, with raptorial anterior legs and very long, slender median and posterior legs. The anterior tarsi are sometimes composed of three segments of variable length or of one segment with one or two claws. The median and posterior tarsi are very short and composed of three segments. The anterior coxæ are long. The eyes are variable but usually prominent and with relatively large and few facets. The antennæ are long and slender, sometimes longer than the body and occasionally with abundant sericeous setæ.

Both alate and apterous forms occur but the presence or absence of wings is not related to sex, and when these appendages are absent, the thorax may exhibit modifications but not the sexual organs. There are no odoriferous glands.

The hemelytra are long and narrow with a narrow corium which may extend along the greater part of the costal margin and even to the apex of the membrane.

The **Emesinæ** are found in many different habitats, in particular in those places which are humid and poorly lighted. Some species have been found in caves but they do not exhibit adaptations to a cavernicolous existence. Species which have been collected in caves include *Myiophanes fluitaria* McAtee and Malloch 1926, *Bagauda lucifugus* McAtee and Malloch 1926, and *Bagauda cavernicola* Paiva 1919, the first two collected in Malaya, the last-mentioned collected in Assam.

A stridulatory furrow is present, so far as is known, in all genera, but is somewhat variable in structure. In some genera it is apparently not striate, *e.g. Guithera* Distant 1906; in others the striations are extremely feeble. Generally the striæ are relatively few in number, coarse and widely separated. In *Stenolœmus plumosus* Stål 1871 and *S. crassirostris* Stål 1871, the striæ become progressively coarser towards the posterior end of the furrow; in *S. marshalli* Distant 1903, *S. decarloi* Wygodzinsky 1947 and *S. bogdanovi* Oshanin 1870, the furrow is coarsely striate in the posterior half only. The furrow is similarly striate in *Eugubinus reticolus* Distant 1915.

Not a great deal is known concerning the ecology of the **Emesinæ**. Their food consists mainly of small insects such as gnats and other small flies which are often present in the places frequented by them.

Those ova which have been examined are mostly cylindrical, somewhat narrow and may have chorionic processes or a long filament. The chorion is generally smooth and may be ribbed or have short scales or spines. The operculum sometimes has a conical elevation. The **Emesinæ** are distributed in all zoogeographical regions. They are nocturnal and are frequently recorded as having been attracted to artificial light.

Visayanocorinæ Miller 1952. In this subfamily are two very small genera, *Visayanocoris* Miller 1952 with one species, *nitens*, and *Carayonia* Villiers 1951 with two species, *culiciformis* Usinger 1952 and *camerunensis* Villiers 1951.

They are characterized by a smooth, shining integument, the head without a transverse sulcus on the vertex, and by having no ocelli. The scutellum has a long, slender apical spine and the anterior tibiæ a flattened acute projection on the inner surface apically. A stridulatory furrow is present. *V. nitens* occurs in the Philippine Islands, *C. culiciformis* in Ceylon and

Fig. 24

Visayanocoris nitens
Miller 1952.
(Visayanocorinæ)

camerunensis in West Africa. Apparently their habitat is the canopy of forest trees.

Saicinæ Stål 1859. Members of this subfamily are mostly fragile, elongate insects with long slender legs and antennæ and with the pronotum and scutellum spinose. Spines are sometimes present on the lower surface of the head. They have prominent eyes with rather large facets. There are no ocelli. The body is minutely pilose or sericeous. Odoriferous glands are apparently absent. A stridulatory furrow is present.

Very little is known about their habits and development. The ovum of an unidentified species that I have examined is cylindrical with one side feebly curved and with a flat operculum. The ovum of *Polytoxus marianensis* Usinger 1946 is oblong oval, broadly rounded on one side and scarcely rounded on the other. It is rounded posteriorly and has the micropylar end carinate around a relatively small operculum. The chorion is glabrous and white. The total length is 0·75 mm. The **Saicinæ** are entirely nocturnal and are distributed in the Old and New Worlds.

Bactrodinæ Stål 1865. Small, slender insects with the hemelytra having only one large cell in the membrane. Other characters are the very slender posterior half of the postocular portion of the head, spined anterior femora, curved anterior tibiæ which are considerably shorter than the femora and the pronotum in which the transverse sulcus is much nearer the anterior than the posterior margin. The third rostral segment is as long as or a little longer than the second segment. A stridulatory furrow is present.

Stenopodinæ Stål 1859. Mostly somewhat narrow, small to large Reduviids of dull colouration, piceous or testaceous. They are characterized by the long antennæ, the usually elongate cylindrical head with a distinct neck, presence of inter-antennal spines and by the venation of the hemelytra which

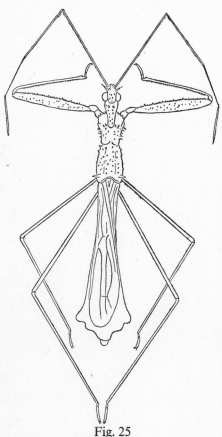

Fig. 25

Bactrodes spinulosus Stål 1862. (Bactrodinæ).

generally have a large discal cell. This type of venation is, however, not constant, the cell being absent and the venation of the corium markedly different in *Anacanthesancus* Miller 1955, *Canthesancus* Amyot and Serville 1843 and *Thodelmus* Stål 1859.

A stridulatory furrow is present and is variable in structure, e.g., in *Aulacogenia* Stål 1870, it is coarsely striate posteriorly but the striations on the anterior part are visible only under high magnification. In some genera, for example, *Oncocephalus* Klug 1830, *Sastrapada* Amyot and Serville 1843, the anterior femora are thick and have rows of spines or tubercles on the lower surface, while in *Padasastra* Villiers 1948, *Staccia* Stål 1865 and *Neostaccia* Miller 1940 moderately long spines are present. A *fossula spongiosa* is absent from all genera except *Canthesancus* and *Anacanthesancus*. Some members of the Duliticorini are strongly spinose, for example, *Echinocoris* Miller 1949 and *Parechinocoris* Miller 1949.

The **Stenopodinæ** are nocturnal in habits and are often attracted to artificial light. So far as is known, the females oviposit in the soil. Ova which have been examined are ovate with the operculum feebly convex, or are subspherical with short chorionic processes. With regard to their being attracted to artificial light, although both sexes are attracted, it seems that the females are not susceptible until after oviposition has taken place. Dorsal glands are present on the fourth and fifth segments of the abdomen in the neanides.

The **Stenopodinæ** are widely distributed, the Old World having by far the larger number of genera.

Tribelocephalinæ Stål 1865, are dull-coloured, mostly dark-brown, black or fulvous insects with dense tomentose clothing on head, body and corium, which conceals to a great extent the actual form of these parts, the head in particular. Fine and moderately long setæ are usually interspersed among the tomentosity, and in some species similar setæ arise from between the facets of the eyes. The hemelytra are ample with a very narrow corium and large membranal cells. Brachypterous females occur in the genera *Tribelocephala* Stål 1853 and *Afrodecius* Jeannel 1919. A stridulatory furrow is present, the striæ being somewhat coarse in certain genera.

Most of the species are included in the two genera *Tribelocephala* and *Opistoplatys* Westwood 1834 but there are some extraordinarily aberrant forms which have been described in the last fifty years. The most bizarre of these are the six oriental genera *Apocaucus* Distant 1909, *Megapocaucus* Miller 1954, *Gastrogyrus* Bergroth 1921, *Acanthorinocoris* Miller 1940, *Matangocoris* Miller 1940 and *Homognetus* Bergroth 1923, all of which differ from *Tribelocephala* and *Opistoplatys* among other things, in having the tarsi composed of

G

two segments and in the particular arrangement of the tomentosity on the head.

Apocaucus and *Megapocaucus* are remarkable for the unusual shape of the head, the vertex being greatly elevated laterally. Abundant, very long curved setæ, more or less fused for the greater part of their length, arise from these elevated areas and conceal the dorsal surface of the head entirely. Another character of these genera is the very considerably reduced corium. So far, only two species are known, *Apocaucus laneus* Distant 1909 and *Megapocaucus laticeps* Miller 1954, the former from India, the latter from Java.

Afrodecius, of which there are six known species, is distributed in Central and West Africa. This genus is remarkable for the unusual form of the rostrum, the second segment of which has a projection or spur on the inner surface apically. The purpose of this spur is unknown, but possibly it may have some connexion with stridulation. The colour pattern of one species of *Afrodecius* agrees to some extent with that of certain Lycidæ (Coleoptera) and it has been suggested that, in view of this, the habits of the genus are diurnal.

A genus even more aberrant than those previously mentioned was described from a single female found on the island of Fernando Poo. This genus, *Xenocaucus* China and Usinger 1949, has tarsi composed of one segment, no wings and no eyes. Another feature is the structure of the basal antennal segment which is concave on its lower surface, the concavity forming a resting place for the remaining segments. It has been suggested that the absence of compound eyes indicates that *Xenocaucus* lives in the soil.

Opistoplatys appears to be a composite genus which could be legitimately divided into two sub-genera, the difference being based on the structure of the head and rostrum mainly, and also the type and abundance of the tomentose clothing. Female *Tribelocephala* and *Opistoplatys* apparently are not active until after oviposition, that is if it is justifiable to infer this from the fact that the females in collections which have been examined have all been found to have completely empty abdomens.

Hardly anything is known of the habits of the **Tribelocephalinæ**, but in the main they appear to be nocturnal. They are often attracted

---

Fig. 26   Neanides of Reduviidæ (*facing*)

1. *Petalochirus umbrosus* Herrich-Schaeffer 1853. Salyavatinæ. Fifth instar.
2. *Centrocnemis* sp. Reduviinæ. Fourth instar.
3. *Cimbus* sp. Ectrichodiinæ. Fourth instar.
4. *Cleontes genitus* Distant 1903. Apiomerinæ. Fifth instar.

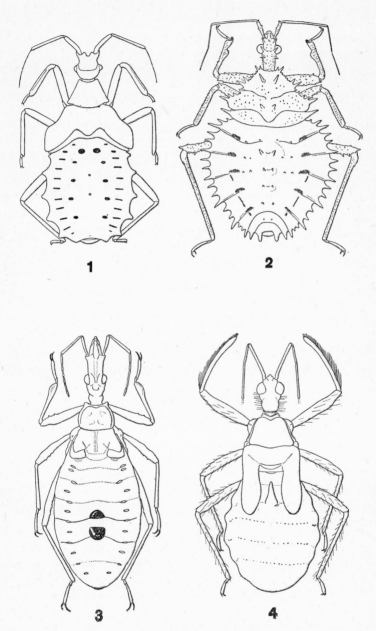

Fig. 26

to artificial light. Occasionally they are found among vegetable debris. The *Tribelocephalinæ* are distributed in the warm regions of the Old World with the exception of Madagascar.

Salyavatinæ Stål 1859, are dull-coloured insects with black or pale yellow spots, particularly on the connexivum. The basal antennal segment is usually moderately thick, the antennal tubercles on the head prominent, the head and pronotum sometimes have long spines and the rostrum is thick and short. A *fossula spongiosa* is present on the anterior and median tibiæ. In *Petalochirus* Palisot Beauvois 1805, *Alvilla* Stål 1874 and *Syberna* Stål 1874, the anterior tibiæ are compressed and expanded. In all genera the anterior tarsi are composed of two segments. The scutellum sometimes has two basal lateral spines or tubercles as well as an apical spine. A stridulatory furrow is present.

The Salyavatinæ are mostly nocturnal but some species of *Petalochirus* are usually found on herbage in the daytime. They are frequently attracted to artificial light.

There appear to be three different types of ovum in this subfamily, the strangest being those of *Petalochirus umbrosus* Herrich Schaeffer 1853 and *Elaphocranum* Bergroth 1904. These resemble a cone flattened on three sides, and with the operculum, which consequently is triangular, also flat. The pole opposite the operculum is also somewhat flattened. The ova of *Petalochirus brachialis* Stål 1858, and of *P. obesus* Miller 1940 and of a species of *Alvilla* Stål 1874 are of another type, being more or less spherical with the operculum pyriform in outline. The ova of some species of *Lisarda* Stål 1859 are sub-ampulliform and somewhat compressed near the apex which results in the operculum being pyriform in outline; but it is feebly convex with a cylindrical elevation.

It is not unusual for Reduviidæ when handled to attempt to pierce the fingers with the stylets. *Petalochirus umbrosus*, however, in my experience has shown no readiness to bite, the only reaction to this kind of treatment being vigorous stridulation and the emission of fluid from the metathoracic glands.

The ostioles of the dorsal abdominal glands in the neanides of *P. umbrosus* and *Lisarda rhodesiensis* Miller 1950 are located at the base of the fourth, fifth and sixth segments.

Little is known of the food preferences of Salyavatinæ. *Lisarda* spp. have been noticed attacking worker termites and also the alate forms in the teak forests of Java. With the exception of one genus, *Salyavata* Amyot and Serville 1843, the Salyavatinæ are distributed in the tropical and sub-tropical regions of the Old World. *Salyavata* is Neotropical.

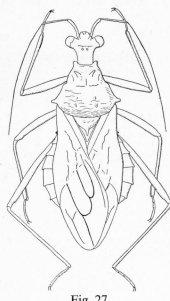

Fig. 27

Eupheno pallens (Laporte).
(Eupheninæ)

Euphenin æ Miller 1955. Up to the present time there is one genus, *Eupheno* Gistel 1848, in this subfamily. It contains three species, *pallens* (Laporte) 1832, *histrionicus* Stål 1862 and *rhabdophorus* Breddin 1898. The subfamily characters are: head transverse; eyes pedunculate; ocelli not elevated; ante-ocular with a bifurcate process; juga produced pronotum with spines and tubercles; scutellum with a spine arising behind the apex; prosternum produced anteriorly; segment six of abdomen obsolete midventrally; segment seven very wide and angulate; segment eight visible; metathoracic glands with two pairs of ostioles, one each in the metasternal depression and adjacent to the coxal cavity and one on each metapleural epimeron, on a lamellar elevation; anterior and median tibiæ with a *fossula spongiosa*; apophyses of female genital segments strongly developed.

Nothing is known, apparently, about the ecology of the species referred to. The structure of the female genital segments suggests that the ova are inserted into some substance or other.

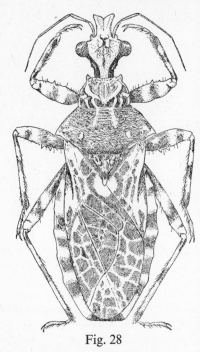

Fig. 28

Cethera marmorata Miller 1950.
(Cetherinæ)

Cetherinæ Jeannel 1919. Members of this subfamily are small, active insects characterized by the more or less pedunculate eyes, elevated ocelli, vertex with a bilobate elevation, tuberculate and spined pronotum, scutellum with an apical spine and sometimes with basal lateral spines, habitus somewhat compressed dorso-ventrally.

The venation of the corium has the following characters: R+M, M+Cu very short; IA meeting Cu at about the middle and continuing to the base of the internal cell of the membrane; IA with a branch vein arising near the apex of the internal cell which is considerably narrower than the external cell. In addition to the pair of metathoracic gland ostioles located in the metasternal depression and adjacent to the inner margin of the acetabulum, there is another pair of ostioles. These are on the metapleural epimeron and near its posterior margin.

Fig. 29   Ova of Reduviidæ (*facing*)

1. *Tydides rufus* Serville 1831. 3·00 mm. Piratinæ.
2. *Santosia macuiata* (Fabricius) 1781. 2·20 mm. Ectrichodiinæ.
3. *Philodoxus principalis* (Distant) 1903. 3·20 mm. Ectrichodiinæ.
4. *Hammacerus cinctipes* (Stål) 1858. 3·00 mm. Hammacerinæ.
5. *Cleontes ugandensis* Distant 1912. 3·30 mm. Apiomerinæ.
6. *Beharus cylindripes* (Fabricius) 1803. 5·00 mm. Apiomerinæ.
7. *Tapirocoris limbatus* Miller 1954. 1·90 mm. Harpactorinæ.
8. *Apiomerus lanipes* (Fabricius) 1803. 3·00 mm. Apiomerinæ.
9. *Rhaphidosoma maximum* Miller 1950. 4·50 mm. Rhaphidosominæ.
10. *Graptoclopius lieftincki* Miller 1954. 3·00 mm. Harpactorinæ.
11. *Acanthiscium* sp. 1·60 mm. Harpactorinæ.
12. *Phonolibes tricolor* Bergroth 1912. 2·70 mm. Phonolibinæ.
13. *Lopodytes nigrescens* Miller 1950. 3·00 mm. Rhaphidosominæ.
14. *Korinchocoris insolitus* Miller 1941. 1·50 mm. Harpactorinæ.
15. *Endochus* sp. 2·00 mm. Harpactorinæ.
16. *Sinea undulata* Uhler 1894. 1·40 mm. Harpactorinæ.
17. *Hæmatolæcha* sp. 1·90 mm. Ectrichodiinæ.

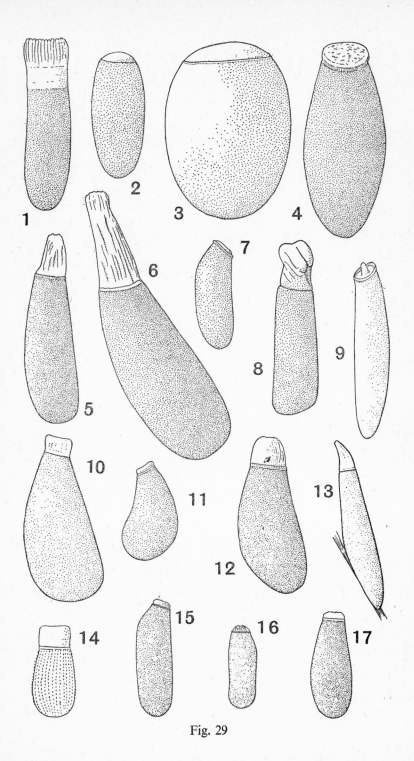

Fig. 29

There are four genera known up to the present time. They are *Cethera* Amyot and Serville 1843, *Cetheromma* Jeannel 1917, *Caridomma* Bergroth 1894, *Carcinomma* Bergroth 1894 and *Caprocethera* Breddin 1903.

The ova of *Carcinomma simile* Horvath 1914 are subspherical with minute chorionic filaments and those of *Cethera musiva* (Germar) 1837 ovate with the anterior end somewhat constricted. Neanides of *Cethera* spp. have been found under logs and stones. The food of both neanides and adults is probably termites. The **Cetherinæ** are confined to the Ethiopian Region and Madagascar.

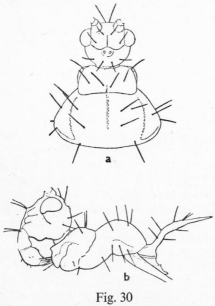

Manangocorinæ Miller 1954. This subfamily which contains one species *Manangocoris horridus* Miller is characterized by the transverse head with the anteocular strongly declivous, almost vertical, small and widely separated ocelli, the tuberculate basal antennal segment, the transverse pronotal lobes in which the anterior lobe is shorter than the posterior lobe, the scutellum with a long apical spine, the membranous hemelytra, the anterior tibiæ incrassate and laterally compressed apically and with no *fossula spongiosa* and by the abundantly setose posterior tibiæ. Nothing is known about its habits.

Fig. 30
Manangocoris horridus Miller 1954.
(Manangocorinæ)

Sphæridopinæ Costa Lima 1940. The characters of representatives of this subfamily are the small head with large eyes narrowly separated at their lower surfaces, a rostrum with a very short and thick basal segment, slender straight second and a very short third segment. In the genus *Volesus* Champion 1899 articulation between the second and third segment is very difficult to define. The median and posterior coxæ are widely separated. Another character is the long stridulatory furrow which is striate, however, only for a little more than half its length anteriorly.

The genera belonging to this subfamily, *Sphæridops* Amyot and Serville 1843 and *Volesus* are Neotropical. The genus *Eurylochus* Torre Bueno 1914 should not be placed in the subfamily.

Physoderinæ Miller 1954. Rather small, dull-coloured Reduviidæ

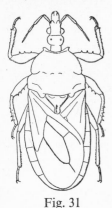

Fig. 31

Physoderes patagiata Miller 1941. (Physoderinæ)

with the following characters: head and body tuberculate, the tubercles low and bearing spatulate setæ; head elongate with a transverse sulcus behind the eyes; ocelli present, rostrum straight with the second segment much longer than segments one and three together; both lobes of the pronotum more or less transverse; scutellum with apex produced, usually flattened and sulcate. Hemelytra complete with the first anal vein forming part of the internal cell of the membrane extended to about the middle of the claval suture and also produced towards the apex of the membrane; vein Cu of the corium obsolescent; Sc not coalescing with R; M not connected with R; R+M diverging at apical margin of the corium; membrane extended backwards along costal margin of corium; anterior and median femora spined on lower surface; *fossula spongiosa* absent; stridulatory furrow present.

The metathoracic wings in representatives of this subfamily are coloured and may be entirely infumate, entirely yellow or infumate with the basal half yellow. There are three genera known at the present time, namely *Physoderes* Westwood 1844, *Neophysoderes* Miller and *Physoderoides* Miller, 1956 the first-named distributed in the Oriental Region, Madagascar and Mauritius, the last two recorded from Madagascar. *Physoderes* spp. are found mainly among decaying vegetable matter. One species, *P. curculionis* China 1935 is said to prey on coleopterous larvæ in decaying banana stems.

The ovum of *Physoderes patagiata* Miller 1941 is cylindrical with one side somewhat shorter than the other and straight. The operculum has, in the centre, a truncate, rounded, cylindrical elevation and the differentiated portion of the chorion is narrow. In colour it is brownish-yellow with the operculum and differentiated portion of the chorion whitish.

Chryxinæ Champion 1898. Small or medium-sized insects. Head much wider and higher than long and strongly declivous anteriorly; sulcus on vertex distinct; ocelli absent or present – in the latter event situated between the eyes; rostrum robust and short, strongly curved; basal segment of the antennæ short and robust, the remaining segments more slender; transverse sulcus on the pronotum situated nearer the apical than the posterior margin; legs simple; tarsi with three segments; hemelytra with a distinct corium; membrane with one cell; abdominal glands present on the third, fourth and fifth segments; stridulatory furrow present.

Fig. 32

Chryxus tomentosus Champion 1898. (Chryxinæ).

This subfamily contains two species, *Chryxus tomentosus* Champion 1898 and *C. travassosi* Lent and Wygodzinsky 1944, the former from Panama, the latter from Brazil. Nothing appears to be known about the ecology of these species.

Vesciinæ Fracker and Bruner 1924. This subfamily contains small dark-coloured insects characterized mainly by the short anteocular portion of the head, the presence or absence of ocelli, eyes with large facets, anterior femora incrassate, anterior tibiæ curved apically. The hemelytra may be fully developed or brachypterous with two cells in the membrane. The anterior pronotal lobe is considerably longer than the posterior lobe and the scutellum is produced apically. A stridulatory furrow is present.

Fig. 33

Vescia adamanta Haviland 1931. (Vesciinæ).

The genera so far known are *Vescia* Stål 1865, *Pessoaia* Costa Lima 1941, *Microvescia* Wygodzinsky 1943, *Mirambulus* Breddin 1901, all Neotropical, *Chopardita* Villiers 1948 from West Africa and the Sudan, and *Eremovescia* Miller 1951 from the Sudan. The last-mentioned was placed in the Vesciinæ in error. There is no information regarding their habits.

Reduviinæ Spinola 1850. This is a large and composite family represented in all zoogeographical regions. It contains many genera, all of which are characterized by the absence of a discal cell in the hemelytra, by the scutellum with an apical spine or tubercle and sometimes with latero-basal spines. The ocelli are well developed except in apterous forms in which they are greatly reduced or absent. The pronotum has a transverse sulcus situated near the middle of the segment. The legs are more or less slender and the tarsi have three segments. Odoriferous glands are usually present in the neanides and are located on the fourth, fifth and sixth dorsal segments. Genera without such glands are *Gerbelius* Distant 1903 and *Durganda* Amyot and Serville 1843. A *fossula spongiosa* is present on both the anterior and median tibiæ in most genera. It is absent from *Psophis* Stål 1863, *Cheronea* Stål 1863, *Nalata* Stål 1858, *Microlestria* Stål 1872, *Euvonymus* Distant 1904, and is present on the anterior tibiæ only of *Voconia* Stål 1865, *Stachyogenys* Stål 1870, *Gerbelius* Distant 1903, *Haplonotocoris* Miller 1940, *Pasira* Stål 1859, *Pasiropsis* Reuter 1881, *Nannolestes* Bergroth 1913, *Heteropinus* Breddin 1903 and *Durganda*. In *Croscius* Stål 1874 it is extremely small and is present on both anterior and median tibiæ. In *Centrocnemis* Signoret 1852 it is short on the anterior tibiæ but somewhat longer on the median tibiæ. Males and females of *Holotrichius* Burmeister 1835 have no *fossula spongiosa* on either anterior or median tibiæ. The species *insularis* Distant 1903 has this organ on the median tibiæ only.

A stridulatory furrow is present in most genera both in the adults and the neanides in a more advanced stage. It is, however, absent from *Psophis* and *Euvonymus*. In *Staliastes* Kirkaldy 1900 the striæ have partly disappeared, e.g. in *S. rufus* Laporte 1832 and *S. zonatus* (Walker) 1873 the furrow has no striæ posteriorly. The striæ are absent from *Staliastes malayanus* Miller 1940 and *Heteropinus*.

The Reduviinæ comprise mostly alate forms but brachypterous forms also occur. In certain genera, namely *Edocla* Stål 1859, *Paredocla* Jeannel 1914 and *Holotrichius*, the females are always apterous, but the males may be fully alate or apterous. In *Diplosiacanthia* Breddin 1903 the females are apterous and both sexes of *Ecmetacantha* Reuter 1882 are brachypterous. Apterous males and females as well as alate males occur in *Psophis*, but so far as is known alate females have not been discovered. Brachypterous and micropterous individuals occur in *Acanthaspis* Amyot and Serville 1843.

As previously stated, the **Reduviinæ** is a composite subfamily containing several genera for which new subfamilies should be made.

Among these may be mentioned the genera with a strongly flattened habitus, a reduced or no stridulatory furrow and widely separated coxæ; for example, *Durganda*, *Staliastes*, *Apechtia* Reuter 1881, *Apechtiella* Miller 1948, *Sminthus* Stål 1865, *Velitra* Stål 1865, all of which pass a part of their lives under the loose bark of dead trees. The females have the apophyses of the genital segments strongly developed forming an ovipositor suitable for the insertion of ova into crevices in decaying bark or wood.

The genus *Centrocnemis* too will have to be removed to a new subfamily in view mainly of its possessing a rostrum composed of four visible segments, and of the great difference in the venation of the hemelytra from that of a typical Reduviine and also on account of its having two pairs of metathoracic glands, one of which is located in the metasternal depression and adjacent to the inner margin of the posterior acetabulum and the other on the meta-pleural epimeron.

The habits of **Reduviinæ** are various. Some genera live in human dwellings, in stables or fowl runs—for example, species of *Reduvius* Lamarck 1801—some under loose bark of dead trees, some in desert or sub-desert areas, namely *Reduvius*, *Parthocoris* Miller 1950 and *Holotrichius*; *Khafra* Distant 1902 has been found in caves but is not a true cavernicolous insect; *Alleocranum biannulipes* Montrouzier and Signoret 1861, a small and strongly setose species, is often found in stored products such as rice, on the insect pests of which it feeds. Its mode of life has brought about its almost cosmopolitan distribution.

The habit of accumulating debris on the body and legs is met with in the genera *Reduvius*, *Acanthaspis* and *Paredocla* and is common to both adults and neanides. This debris which may con-sist of soil fragments, remains of insect prey or of vegetable matter, adheres to the secretory hairs from which a glutinous substance flows. It is still a complete mystery what purpose this masking of the body with debris serves, since the genera which have the habit live almost entirely in concealment in secluded and dark places. The opinion is expressed sometimes that the disguise is an aid in the capture of prey and also that it is protective against enemies. Nevertheless, the accumulating of debris is deliberate and not fortuitous as may be proved by removing it and then allowing the denuded bug access to similar material. Within a few minutes it will restore the mantle of debris by casting it on the body with its legs.

Reduviinæ appear to be general feeders and will attack most Arthropods within certain size limits. There is little information of species confining themselves to one sort of prey. *Phonergates bicoloripes* Stål 1855 is said to prey on ticks and *Reduvius personatus*

Linnæus 1758 to feed on the bed-bug, but it is not known whether ticks and bed-bugs respectively are the sole kinds of food sought by these two Reduviids.

Platymerus rhadamanthus Gerstaecker 1873, a large black species with red markings, has been reported as preying on adults of the coconut beetle *Oryctes monocerus* Oliver in Zanzibar. The saliva secreted by both the neanides and adults of this Reduviine is highly virulent, consequently a bite can be extremely painful and its effect may last for several days.

Reduviinæ deposit their ova usually without a glutinous covering in the soil, among vegetable debris or in crevices in the bark of trees. The ova known up to the present are mainly ovoid or cylindrical with a smooth chorion and feebly convex operculum. Exceptions are the ova of *Psophis consanguinea* Distant 1903, which have a large differentiated portion which is also reticulate with the upper margins deflected, the ova of *Pasiropsis vidua* Miller 1954 which are cylindrical with long chorionic filaments, the ova of *Centrocnemis signoreti* Stål 1863 and of *Durganda rubra* Amyot and Serville 1843, subampulliform. Other cylindrical ova are those of *Sminthus* spp., *Dyakocoris vulnerans* (Stål) 1863, *Velitra alboplagiata* Stål 1859 and of *Velitra rubropicta* Amyot and Serville 1843, the last-mentioned with a minutely granulose chorion, and those of *Sminthus* spp. have moderately long chorionic filaments. The ovum of *Dyakocoris* has a more or less flat operculum with an irregularly truncate median elevation and the differentiated portion is short. The ovum of *Korinchocoris insolitus* Miller 1941 has a rather long differentiated portion similar to that of ova of Harpactorinæ. It also has minute curved, prominent setæ on the chorion.

Triatominæ Jeannel 1919. This subfamily contains the most important of all the Reduviidæ. Its members are exclusively predaceous on mammalian and avian blood and are vectors in the Neotropical Region of a malady known as Chagas disease (or American trypanosomiasis) which has effects on human beings similar to those of sleeping sickness, a scourge of some areas of tropical Africa.

The **Triatominæ** are characterized by the elongate head, straight rostrum, complete or partial absence of the transverse sulcus on the vertex and the absence of neanidal glands. A stridulatory furrow is usually present. In the adults, according to Brindley, the 'stink gland passes laterally into a groove which runs along the internal face of the emarginated edge of the metacoxal cavity . . . and communicates with the exterior by a small pore'.

The **Triatominæ** are mostly sombre-coloured insects with sometimes red or yellow markings. *Triatoma rubrofasciata* (de Geer) is tropicopolitan, *T. migrans* Breddin 1903 has been recorded from

Malaysia, but the remaining species are predominately American. Another species found outside America is the Indian *Linshcosteus carnifex* Distant 1904. The affinities of this species to other Triatominæ are problematic; it has no *fossula spongiosa* and the rostrum does not extend beyond the posterior margin of the eyes, consequently there is no stridulatory furrow.

Triatoma rubrofasciata, it has been alleged, is responsible in some measure for the propagation of Kala Azar or oriental sore. This unpleasant condition and Chagas disease are not the result of trypanosomes being injected when the bug is feeding. The disease-provoking organisms are present in the fæces of the bug and when the patient scratches or rubs the spot at which irritation has been set up by the bite, he introduces them into the blood-stream. The relation of **Triatominæ** to mammals and birds is more fully dealt with in the chapter 'Heteroptera associated with mammals and birds'.

Piratinæ Stål 1859. Mostly black or piceous Reduviids. Some species are partly yellow and red with a portion of the legs similarly coloured. The principal characters are the somewhat elongate head, the pronotum longer than wide, anterior and median tibæ with a *fossula spongiosa* which, in some genera, for example, *Ectomocoris* Mayr 1865, may extend almost the entire length of the tibia. The anterior coxæ are usually longer than wide and flattened on the outer surface. The *fossula spongiosa* may, incidentally, extend beyond the apex of the tibia. Alary polymorphism occurs in some genera. Dorsal glands are present in the neanides on abdominal segments three, four and five. The bite of some species is extremely painful, and may give rise to suppurating sores.

Piratinæ are nocturnal and in the daytime seek secluded places under stones and in crevices. They are often attracted to artificial light. So far as is known, the ova are deposited by the female in the soil. Those which have been examined are ovate with a smooth chorion and with fairly long chorionic processes. No definite information is available regarding their food preferences. They appear to be general feeders. *Fusius rubricosus* Stål 1855 has been found in fresh cow-dung in which it was probably seeking coleopterous and dipterous larvæ. This species is widely distributed in the Ethiopian Region. The **Piratinæ** are widely distributed in both the Old and New Worlds.

Phimophorinæ Handlirsch 1897. A subfamily containing a single genus and species, *Phimophorus spissicornis* Bergroth 1886. This is a small Reduviid with a somewhat flattened habitus. The body is granulose and has the longer setæ serrulate. The head is moderately elongate with spiniferous tubercles on each side of the gular region and with the dorsal surface granulose. The antennæ are short and robust, particularly the basal segment which also is sub-rectangular. The eyes and ocelli are small. Rostrum straight with the basal segment much longer than segments two and three together. Legs short and granulose, the tibiæ laterally compressed with a short *fossula spongiosa*. Hemelytra somewhat wide with the membrane containing three cells. A stridulatory furrow is present.

This species, which was originally described by Bergroth as an Aradid, is a somewhat aberrant Reduviid, the systematic position of which is not entirely clear. It has been figured by Wygodzinsky who has also discussed its systematic position without, however, coming to a definite conclusion. I have not been able to obtain a specimen from which a figure could be prepared. Nothing is known of the ecology of this insect, which comes from the Neotropical Region.

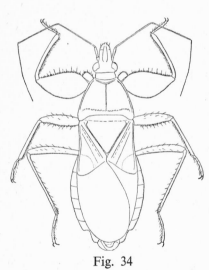

Fig. 34

Pachynomus biguttulus Stål 1863.
(Pachynominæ).

Pachynominæ Stål 1873. Formerly included in the Nabidæ, but on account of the morphological identity of almost all their characters, are now considered to belong to the Reduviidæ. They have the same type of male genitalia and similar odoriferous glands as the Reduviidæ, but the rostrum is composed of four visible segments. There is no stridulatory furrow; ocelli are present but reduced in some genera and the antennæ are composed of five segments. A very small *fossula spongiosa* is present on the anterior and median tibiæ. In *Pachynomus* Klug 1830, *Camarochilus* Harris 1930 and *Punctius* Stål 1873 the ocelli are greatly reduced; in *Aphelonotus* Uhler 1894 they are relatively large.

Pachynomus has very strongly incrassate anterior femora, the lower surface of which is armed with abundant short, slender denticles which are rounded apically. The anterior and median tibiæ and the median femora are similarly armed, the denticles on the tibiæ being short and rounded. The **Pachynominæ** are distributed in parts of Europe, Asia and Africa.

Hammacerinæ Stål 1859. This subfamily contains two genera, *Microtomus* Illiger 1807 and *Homalocoris* Perty 1833, both of which exhibit a remarkable type of antennal structure not to be found in any other Heteroptera. The first antennal segment is short and robust and the second segment is divided into many segments, from eight to forty. Other characters are the prominent eyes and ocelli which are located between them. A stridulatory furrow is present. Dorsal glands of the neanides are on the third, fourth and fifth segments. The **Hammacerinæ** comprise mostly dark-coloured insects with whitish stripes or yellowish spots and are confined to South America, Mexico and the southern parts of the United States. Little is known about the ecology of this subfamily apart from the fact that the habitat is under loose bark of decaying trees. The ovum of *Hammacerus cinctipes* Stål 1858 is elliptical with a flat operculum.

Ectrichodiinæ Spinola 1850. A moderately large subfamily represented in the tropics of the Old and New Worlds. Its members are mostly robust with a thick integument which may be glabrous or strongly sculptured, particularly the dorsal surface of the abdomen of apterous forms. The ventral surface is often carinulate intersegmentally. The hemelytra are complete, but the division between the corium and the membrane is often indistinct. A stridulatory furrow is present. The rostrum is thick and curved in most genera but is straight in *Cimbus* Hahn 1831, *Katanga* Schouteden 1903,

---

Plate 4 (*facing*)

Reduviidæ

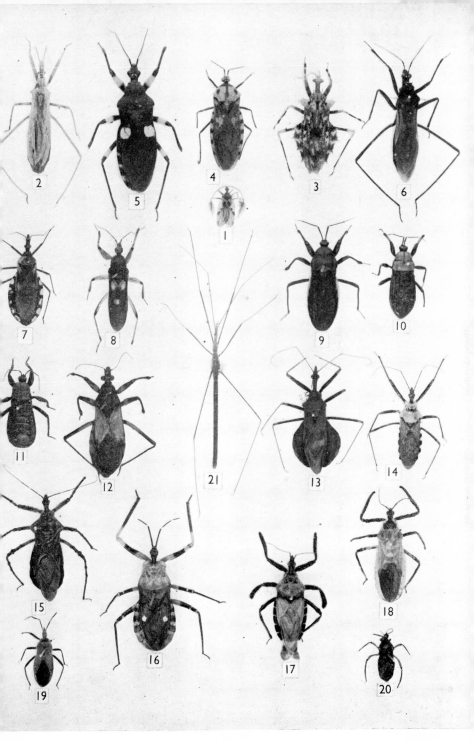

Plate IV

Afrocastra Breddin 1903 and *Katangana* Miller 1954. A rostrum differing very considerably from the curved and straight types is that of *Xenorhyncocoris caraboides* Miller 1938 from Sumatra and *X. princeps* Miller 1948 from Malaya. In *princeps* it is thick, strongly curved at the extreme base of the basal segment which is also somewhat compressed dorso-ventrally. The second segment is more or less normal, that is to say, cylindrical but the external surface is flattened. The third segment is somewhat compressed laterally. In *caraboides* the basal segment is sinuate and strongly compressed dorso-ventrally, the second segment is strongly swollen and feebly laterally compressed, the third segment somewhat compressed laterally.

It is also of note that the prosternum in these two species is strongly produced posteriorly (beyond the base of the mesosternum) consequently the stridulatory area is very long.

The number of antennal segments in **Ectrichodiinæ** varies from four to eight, but no known genus, however, has five segments. The scutellum is usually more or less quadrate with two or three apical spines, the lateral ones usually widely separated except in a few genera. The legs, particularly the anterior and median femora, are robust and may have spines on the lower surface. In some species the anterior femora and trochanters have a raised shagreened area on the lower surface. This affords an additional aid in the gripping powers of the *fossula spongiosa* which are present on the anterior tibiæ of most genera.

Odoriferous glands are present but their position and number are not constant. For example, in *Philodoxus* Horvath 1914 and *Toxopeusiana* Miller 1954 there is only one on the fifth segment; in *Cimbus* there is a gland on the fourth and fifth segments. In *Marœnaspis* Karsch 1892 it is difficult at first sight to locate the position of the glands since the ostiole on segment four is very small, and at the base of segment six is a sclerotized plate scarcely separated from the dorsal plate on segment five. This is a much larger plate with the ostioles transverse. Usually the ostioles are at the base of the fifth and sixth segments. In *Paravilius* Miller 1955 and *Xenorhyncocoris*, *Glymmatophora* Stål 1853 and *Ectrichodia distincta* Signoret 1858 the ostioles are similarly located.

The kind of odour of the fluid from the neanides and adults does not appear to have been noted with the exception of that from *Marœnaspis corallinus* Miller 1950 which resembles verbena. The prey of the majority of the genera is unknown. Some genera, for example, *Ectrichodia* Lepeletier and Serville 1825, *Marœnaspis*, *Scadra* Stål 1859 appear to be restricted in their choice of food, however, and feed only on Myriapoda. This is a curious fact seeing

H

that the body fluids of these Arthropoda have corrosive properties. Many of the **Ectrichodiinæ** are brightly coloured, mainly red and yellow but many also are entirely black or piceous with a violaceous or greenish metallic tinge.

The **Ectrichodiinæ** are mainly nocturnal but may occasionally be seen during the daytime in bright sunshine. Apterous forms *e.g.*, *Glymmatophora* sometimes leave their usual habitat under logs and stones and move about in the open. These excursions are not always voluntary but may be provoked by an invasion of predatory ants. Alary polymorphism is frequent, the reduction or absence of wings being confined mostly to the females, but both alate and apterous males as well as apterous females have been recorded, for example in the genus *Marænaspis*. Genera in which an apterous condition occurs include *Glymmatophora, Mindarus* Stål 1859, *Xenorhyncocoris, Distirogaster* Horvath 1914, *Hæmatorrhopus* Stål 1874, *Katanga, Afrocastra*, and *Katangana*. Brachypterous forms appear in the genus *Ectrychotes* Burmeister 1835.

Oviposition takes place in the soil, the ova being placed in a loose mass without the addition of any glutinous substance. A species of *Scadra* in Malaya envelops the ovum in a whitish gelatinous substance which subsequently hardens. The ova of **Ectrichodiinæ,** so far as is known, are sub-spherical, ovate or elliptical without sculpturation and with a feebly convex operculum.

Perissorhynchinæ Miller 1952. This subfamily contains only one genus, *Perissorhynchus* Miller 1952 which has the following characters: rostrum straight with the basal segment very short,

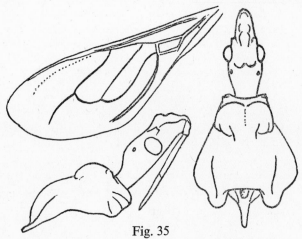

Fig. 35

Perissorhynchus lloydi Miller 1952. (Perissorhynchinæ)

segments two and three almost equal in length, almost entirely membranous hemelytra with the corium extended nearly to the apex of the membrane; a stridulatory furrow is present. There is one species, *lloydi* Miller 1952 from West Africa. Nothing is known about its ecology.

Rhaphidosominæ Jeannel 1919. The characters of this subfamily are: a slender elongate body, long slender antennæ and legs, cylindrical head, small eyes and ocelli (the ocelli may be absent) and a straight rostrum with the second segment the longest. A stridulatory furrow is present. In *Lopodytes* Stål 1853, and *Hoffmannocoris* China 1940 both sexes are alate and in *Rhaphidosoma* Amyot and Serville 1843 and *Leptodema* Carlini 1892, neither is alate.

The **Rhaphidosominæ** are confined to the desert areas or savannahs of the Old World and are to be found mostly among grasses or on low bushes. The females oviposit on plant stems and affix their elongate, cylindrical ova singly at an angle to the substratum. Nothing definite is known of the food of the members of this subfamily. The long, straight rostrum suggests that they may seek their prey – such as lepidopterous stem-borers – living in plants. The secretion from the glands of the adults of *Rhaphidosoma circumvagans* Stål 1855 is very pungent and often reveals their presence among herbage. The ostioles of the glands in the neanides of this species are located at the base of the fourth and fifth segments.

Harpactorinæ Spinola 1850. All the zoogeographical regions have representatives of this subfamily which contains more genera than any other subfamily of the REDUVIIDAE. The principal characters are: rostrum composed of three visible segments and usually curved, but straight in a few genera; ocelli usually small and often elevated; long slender antennæ of four segments but with an intercalary segment sometimes between the basal segments; well-developed hemelytra with a quadrate cell on the corium; legs more or less slender or nodulose, spinose or tuberculate; stridulatory furrow present in most but not all genera; secretory hairs present on the body and legs in some genera, among which *Rhinocoris* Hahn 1834, *Paramphibolus* Reuter 1887, *Peprius* Stål 1859, *Cosmolestes* Stål 1866. The hairs are present in both neanides and adults and it is rare not to find them with a good deal of vegetable or other debris adhering to them, a condition which would appear to be embarrassing rather than useful. Alary polymorphism is infrequent and is confined to the genera *Coranus* Curtis 1833 and *Dicrotelus* Erichson 1842.

Dorsal glands are present on the third, fourth and fifth segments and the dorsal plates are mostly quadrate or ovate in outline. Exaggerated forms of dorsal plates are present in *Pantoleistes*

Stål 1853 in which they are elongate and conical. The actual position of the ostioles of the glands can be confirmed only by preparing specimens in KOH. It is usually stated that in the **Harpactorinæ** these ostioles are on the third, fourth and fifth segments. Actually they are at the base of the fourth, fifth and sixth segments, and in *Rhinocoris albopunctatus* Stål 1855, for example, the ostiole on segment four is located at some distance from the basal margin of the segment, that on segment five is less distant and the ostiole on segment six is on the basal margin. In *Coranus carbonarius* Stål 1855, *Rhinocoris segmentarius* Germar 1837 and *Phonoctonus nigrofasciatus* Stål 1855 the ostiole is at the base of the fourth, fifth and sixth segments. In *R. segmentarius* I have found the vestiges of the gland in the adult.

A stridulatory furrow is absent from the genus *Aphonocoris* Miller 1950. In *Piestolestes* Bergroth 1912 the prosternum has an extremely narrow median sulcus but striæ are apparently absent.

Many **Harpactorinæ** have irregular patches or linear elevated areas composed of a white wax-like substance on the head, body and corium. This substance may be seen in *Peprius*, *Rhinocoris*, *Aprepolestes* Stål, *Acanthiscium* Amyot and Serville 1843 and several others. The function of this substance has not yet been explained, but it may possibly be connected with ecdysis. There are many forms represented in the **Harpactorinæ**. Striking peculiarities

Fig. 36.   Ova of Reduviidæ-Harpactorinæ (*facing*)

1. *Helonotus versicolor* Distant 1912. 2·00 mm.
2. *Vesbius* sp. 1·10 mm.
3. *Heza sphinx* Stål 1863. 2·30 mm.
4. *Cargasdama noualhieri* Villiers 1951. 1·60 mm.
5. *Rhinocoris nitidulus* (Fabricius) 1781. 3·40 mm.
6. *Cydnocoris* sp. 2·00 mm.
7. *Macracanthopsis nodipes* Reuter 1881. 1·20 mm.
8. *Henricohahnia wahnschaffei* Breddin 1900. 2·40 mm.
9. *Paracydnocoris distinctus* Miller 1953. 2·70 mm.
10. Egg mass of *Isyndus heros* (Fabricius) 1803, showing exit hole of hymenopterous parasite.
11. *Henricohahnia vittata* Miller 1954. 2·40 mm.
12. *Villanovanus dichrous* (Stål) 1863. 2·20 mm.
13. *Rihirbus barbarus* Miller 1941. 1·60 mm.
14. *Polydidus* sp. 1·60 mm.
15. *Kibatia* sp. 1·40 mm.
16. *Repipta fuscipes* Stål 1855. 2·20 mm.
17. *Notocyrtus depressus* Stål 1872. 1·70 mm.
18. *Zavattariocoris senegambiæ* Miller 1954. 2·10 mm.
19. *Sphagiastes ramentaceus* (Germar) 1837. 3·00 mm.
20. *Nacorusana nigrescens* Miller 1954. 2·00 mm.
21. *Margasus afzelii* Stål 1855. 2·50 mm.

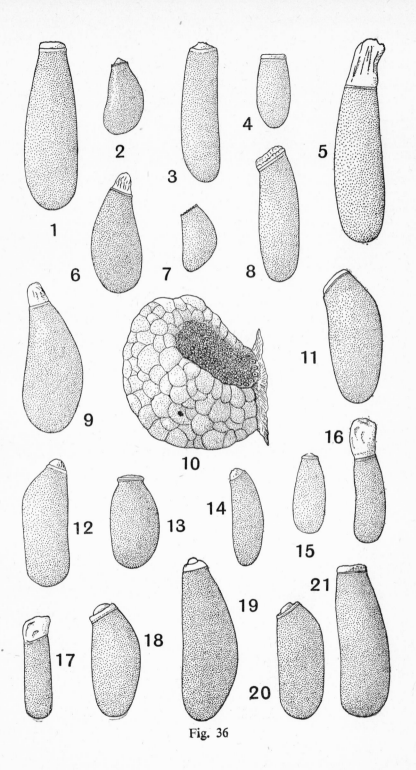

Fig. 36

in structure are seen in *Arilus* Hahn 1831 (Neotropical), which has the pronotum strongly elevated with the denticles on the margin of the elevation; *Notocyrtus* Burmeister 1835 (Neotropical) has the pronotum swollen and concealing the scutellum. In *Sava* Amyot and Serville 1843 (Neotropical) the pronotum is strongly gibbose and produced posteriorly to cover almost the whole abdomen. Its margins are tuberculately produced. In this genus also the prosternum is produced posteriorly beyond the anterior coxæ and thus is longer, probably, than in any other Harpactorine genus. In the Oriental genus *Panthous* Stål 1863, the pronotum is produced posteriorly concealing the scutellum. *Sphagiastes* Stål 1853 has a strongly spinose pronotum with some of the spines arising from elevations. The connexival segments are strongly produced, flattened and spinose.

Many brightly coloured genera are found in this family. Among these may be mentioned *Havinthus* Stål 1859 (Australia), *Vitumnus* Stål 1864, *Callilestes* Stål 1866 and *Rhinocoris* (Palæarctic, Ethiopian and Oriental) of which *Rhinocoris imperialis* Stål 1859 is probably the most striking, the peculiarly hymenopteroid *Acanthiscium* and *Cosmonyttus* Stål 1867 (Neotropical), *Eulyes* Amyot and Serville 1843 (Oriental) and *Phonoctonus nigrofasciatus* Stål (Ethiopian).

Harpactorinæ are diurnal and both adults and neanides frequent flowers to which their prey is attracted, or they roam over bushes and herbage in search of lepidopterous larvæ. *Rhinocoris fuscipes* (Fabricius) 1787, an abundant and widely distributed species in South-East Asia, is often found on *Polanisia viscosa* (a plant with sticky hairs) feeding on insects trapped thereon. *Cosmolestes picticeps* Stål 1859, also a common species in the same region, frequents *Passiflora fœtida*, a low plant possessing bracts with sticky hairs to which other insects become attached.

I have stated that the **Harpactorinæ** are diurnal, but there is, however, one exception, *Hediocoris tibialis* Stål 1855, a brightly coloured species distributed throughout tropical Africa. I have taken this species at light. It is noteworthy that it has large and somewhat prominent ocelli reminiscent of those of some exclusively nocturnal genera belonging to other subfamilies.

As a rule **Harpactorinæ** are found mostly on low vegetation, but certain species, namely *Pantoleistes princeps* Stål 1853 and *Nagusta subflava* Distant 1903 have been found on branches at some distance from the ground, the former at about twenty feet and the latter at eight feet. Another habitat recorded is that under the loose bark of dead trees. Here adults of *Havinthus pentatomus* Herrich-Schaeffer 1853 and neanides of *Sphagiastes* have been found. It is not improbable that *Henricohahnia* Breddin 1900, *Nyllius* Stål 1859,

Orgetorixa China 1925 and allied genera, at least in the neanidal stages, live in such a habitat. The genus *Piestolestes*, to judge by its flattened habitus, is probably another sub-corticolous Reduviid. In the female the genital segments are somewhat produced and seem to be adapted for the insertion of ova into soft material. **Harpactorinæ** are active insects and fly readily when disturbed. The flight is sustained for a short while only. Some fall to the ground from the plant on which they were resting on the approach of danger.

The food of **Harpactorinæ** consists of other insects and their larvæ. There are recorded instances of adults devouring their own ova. I have noticed more specialized feeding in Southern Rhodesia in the case of *Rhinocoris albopunctatus, R. segmentarius* and *R. neavei* Bergroth 1912, the prey being honeybees. Genera which have the second and third segments of the rostrum straight, such as *Henricohahnia, Dicrotelus, Orgetorixa, Nyllius* Stål and allies and *Vadimon* Stål 1865 may possibly prey on larvæ living in burrows, the shape of the rostrum lending itself to probing. Prey is captured by seizing it with the anterior legs and piercing it with the stylets. When the victim has succumbed to the effects of the saliva and is inert, the bug continues to carry it attached to the rostrum until it has completely absorbed the body-fluids, whereupon the prey is released. The saliva is virulent and has been noted as being particularly so in *Coranus carbonarius* and species of *Rhinocoris*.

With regard to oviposition, a large number, probably the majority of **Harpactorinæ**, deposit their ova in groups containing variable numbers from three or four to a hundred or so. Some species arrange their ova in single rows (*Coranopsis vittata* Horvath 1892) or in parallel rows (*Vitumnus scenicus* Stål 1865) or singly (*Peprius pictus* Miller 1950). *Phonoctonus nigrofasciatus* arranges its ova in rings round a plant stem. All these species are Ethiopian. In the case of those species that deposit their ova in groups, the female secretes a glutinous substance and spreads it over the ova forming the periphery of the mass. This substance may afford some protection against parasitization by Hymenoptera.

A special kind of method of arrangement of ova is practised by *Isyndus heros* (Fabricius) 1803, a Malaysian species. This Reduviid, when about to oviposit, secretes a substance in the form of bubbles which rapidly harden and form together a sub-structure into which the ova are extruded and grouped close together with the longer axis vertical. The ova are entirely enclosed except for the opercula. This type of egg-mass might, with some justification, be termed an ootheca. It might be imagined that when the ova are almost entirely covered in this manner they would be protected from the depredations of hymenopterous parasites, but this is not always the case. When parasites, on reaching the adult stage, emerge from the mass, it is a curious fact that they do not select the shortest and easiest route, that is, upwards through the ovum, but they gnaw a passage through the sub-structure. The ova of other species of *Isyndus* have not yet been described.

The ova of **Harpactorinæ** do not exhibit a great variety of form, most of them being cylindrical, straight or feebly curved, or ampulliform to a varying degree. The differentiated portion surrounding the operculum is sometimes relatively long, notably in the ovum of some *Rhinocoris* species. Some of the genera producing ampulliform ova and placing them singly or in very small groups, attach the ovum by one side so that the longer axis is more or less parallel to the substratum. Certain ova, particularly those deposited in compact groups, have a very complicated operculum. A good example of this is the operculum of *Rhinocoris neavei*. This is a hollow cylinder constricted near the base and apex with a small

Fig. 37. Ova of Reduviidæ, Nabidæ, Miridæ, Tingidæ,
Schizopteridæ, Microphysidæ, Belostomatidæ (*facing*)

1. *Gminatus wallengreni* Stål 1859. 1·50 mm. Reduviidæ-Harpactorinæ.
2. *Hiranetis* sp. 1·80 mm. Reduviidæ-Harpactorinæ.
3. *Vadimon bergrothi* Montandon 1892. 1·60 mm. Reduviidæ-Harpactorinæ.
4. *Sclomina erinacea* Stål 1861. 2·00 mm. Reduviidæ-Harpactorinæ.
5. *Nagusta* sp. 1·50 mm. Reduviidæ-Harpactorinæ.
6. *Campsolomus strumulosus* Stål 1870. 1·30 mm. Reduviidæ-Harpactorinæ.
7. *Pirnonota convexicollis* Stål 1859. 1·30 mm. Reduviidæ-Harpactorinæ.
8. *Arbela* sp. 1·70 mm. Nabidæ-Nabinæ.
9. *Gorpis papuanus* Harris 1939. 3·00 mm. Nabidæ-Gorpinæ.
10. *Psilistus chinai* Harris 1937. 2·40 mm. Nabidæ-Prostemminæ.
11. *Nabicula subcoleoptratus* Kirby 1837. 2·00 mm. Nabidæ-Nabinæ.
12. *Strongylocoris leucocephalus* Linnæus 1761. 2·50 mm. Miridæ-Orthotylinæ.
13. *Calocoris* sp. Miridæ-Mirinæ.
14. *Dictyonota stichnocera* Fieber 1844. 3·00 mm. Tingidæ-Tinginæ.
(after Butler).
15. *Vilhennanus angolensis* Wygodzinsky 1950. · 75 mm. Schizopteridæ.
(after Wygodzinsky).
16. *Myrmedobia tenella* Zetterstedt 1840. 0.47 mm. Microphysidæ.
(after Carayon).
17. *Lethocerus indicum* (Lepeletier and Serville) 1825. 3·70 mm.
Belostomatidæ.
18. *Agraptocorixa eurynome* (Kirkaldy) 1922. Corixidæ. (after Hale).
19. *Cymatia americana* Hussey 1922. Corixidæ.
20. *Sigara* (*Vermicorixa*) *alternata* (Say) 1825. Corixidæ. (after Hungerford).
21. *Trichocorixa verticalis* (Fieber) 1851. Corixidæ.
22. *Nepa apiculata* Uhler 1862. Nepidæ.
23. *Ranatra fusca* Palisot Beauvois 1805. Nepidæ.
24. *Hydrometra martini* Kirkaldy 1900. 1·00 mm. Hydrometridæ.
25. *Gerris* sp. Gerridæ.
26. *Plea striola* Fieber 1844. Pleidæ.
27. *Gclastocoris oculatus* (Fabricus) 1798. Gelastocoridæ.
28. *Mesovelia mulsanti* White 1879. Veliidæ.
29. *Salda anthracina* Uhler 1877. Saldidæ.
30. *Notonecta irrorata* Uhler 1878. Notonectidæ.

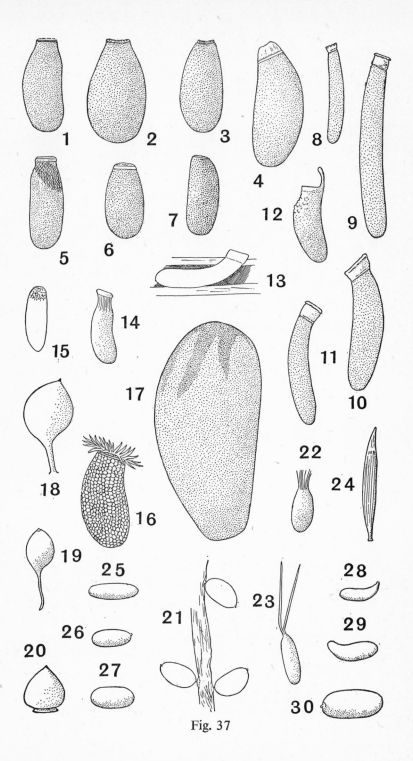

Fig. 37

reticulate area basally. The apical margin is recurved, fimbriate or dentate. Within the cylinder is the opercular process, bluntly conical with filaments apically and with the surface minutely punctate and reticulate. In ova having this type of operculum the differentiated portion of the chorion is reflexed apically and covers the apex of the cylinder. The object of this type of operculum is to allow air to penetrate the ovum. Ova are also deposited in a group by *Panthous dœdalus* Stål 1863, and they are covered by the female with a glutinous substance. Neanides hatching from ova deposited in groups are usually gregarious until after the first ecdysis when they disperse and begin to feed. Since the duration of the first instar is short, abstention from food is apparently unimportant. It is possible that moisture in the form of dew or raindrops is imbibed occasionally.

Apiomerinæ Stål 1859. A subfamily containing many genera, all of them distributed in the Nearctic, Neotropical and Ethiopian Regions. Most of them are dull in colour, but some species, namely *Apiomerus binotatus* Champion 1899, *A. elatus* Stål 1862, *A. fasciatus* Herrich-Schaeffer 1848, *A. elegans* Distant 1903 and *Ponerobia bipustulata* (Fabricius) 1781 have red and yellow markings. *Apiomerus vexillarius* Champion 1899, *A. geniculatus* Erichson 1848, *A. ochropterus* Stål 1866 and *A. pilipes* (Fabricius) 1787 have two red foliaceous expansions arising from the eighth abdominal segment. In *A. nigrolobus* Stål 1872 these expansions are black.

The **Apiomerinæ** are characterized by long anterior tibiæ which, like the median and posterior pair are strongly setose. The anteocular is not much shorter than the postocular, the latter being somewhat widened in the region of the ocelli which are lateral in position. A stridulatory furrow is present in all genera. The anterior and median tarsi are very short and when not in use rest in a sulcus on the upper surface of the tibia, the sulcus varying in depth; for example, in *Ponerobia* Amyot and Serville 1843 it is very shallow. In *Micrauchenius* Amyot and Serville 1843 there is no sulcus. In most genera the median tarsi are normal but, in *Heniartes* Spinola 1837 they are very short. *Amauroclopius* Stål 1868 has extremely small anterior tarsi.

The Ethiopian genera *Rhodainiella* Schouteden 1913, *Diaspidius* Westwood 1857 and *Cleontes* Stål 1874 are mainly whitish or dark yellow with black legs and antennæ. Incidentally, it is doubtful if these three genera have been correctly assigned to the **Apiomerinæ**. A closer study of them will, I think, show that the erection of a new subfamily to receive them will be required. In *Diaspidius* and *Rhodainiella* the tibiæ are sulcate on the outer surface apically. In this sulcus the tarsus can be lodged. *Cleontes* has no anterior tarsi.

The habit of covering the anterior tibiæ with a resin for the purpose of capturing prey is characteristic of some members of this subfamily, but how many practise this method is not known. Specimens in collections are often found to have a considerable amount of vegetable and other debris adhering to them on account of a glutinous material on their legs and body. Whether this substance is secreted by the insect or is deliberately collected by it is not always clear. The actual collection of a resinous substance by a member of this subfamily was observed in the case of *Beharus lunatus* Lepeletier and Serville 1825 in Surinam by Uittenboogaart.

Some genera, among which *Heniartes*, have small patches of a white wax-like substance on the body similar to those to be seen in many Harpactorinæ. It is not known how or from where this is produced. Possibly it may have covered a much greater area of the insect prior to the final ecdysis and may, indeed, have played a rôle in that operation. The Apiomerinæ are diurnal and frequent foliage and flowers.

The ova and developmental stages of some species of *Apiomerus* Hahn 1831 and *Heniartes* have been studied. *Apiomerus spissipes* (Say) 1825 and *Heniartes jaakkoi* Wygodzinsky 1947 deposit their ova in a mass, the former covering the ova forming the outer row of the mass with a moderate amount of glutinous substance. The latter embeds them in a copious quantity of the same kind of substance so that the shape is entirely concealed. The substance is secreted in a spongy state but it rapidly becomes hard. The ova of known species of **Apiomerinæ** are cylindrical with a differentiated portion similar to that of **Harpactorinæ**. Dorsal glands are present in the neanides of the Neotropical representatives of the **Apiomerinæ** on the third, fourth and fifth segments. Very little is known regarding the habits and ecology of the Ethiopian members of the subfamily. According to Schouteden the neanides of *Cleontes* are found mainly under the loose bark of trees, and on account of the viscous substance which covers them, a great quantity of debris accumulates on them. The ovum of *Cleontes ugandensis* Distant 1912 is cylindrical with a moderately long differentiated portion.

Dorsal glands in the neanides of *Diaspidius* and *Rhodainiella* are located on the fourth and fifth abdominal segments; in *Cleontes* a single gland ostiole is present on the third segment. In the adult, the position on the dorsum of the abdomen of the gland is indicated by a sub-erect tubercle.

Ectinoderinæ Stål 1866. This subfamily contains three genera: *Ectinoderus* Westwood 1843, *Amulius* Stål 1865 and *Parapanthous* Distant 1919, which are confined to the Indo-Australian Region.

These genera resemble each other in general habitus, having the pronotum greatly expanded posteriorly, but since it has an incision medially, it does not entirely conceal the scutellum. The connexivum is also expanded. A stridulatory furrow is absent. The anteocular portion of the head is very short, the postocular considerably longer and transversely enlarged in the ocellar region. The ocelli are small and lateral. The hemelytra are fully developed and have a large discal cell.

In the three genera mentioned, the anterior tibiæ are thick and strongly setose and the anterior tarsi are composed of one segment with considerably modified claws. *Ectinoderus* and *Amulius* and, so far as is known, *Parapanthous* obtain their prey with the anterior tibiæ to which they apply a resinous substance yielded by certain trees among which *Pinus merkusii* and *Agathis alba*. With the tibiæ thus covered they lie in wait, usually with the body directed downwards on a tree trunk. More details of this exceptional method of capture by these Reduviids will be found in the chapter 'The Legs of Heteroptera'. With regard to the genus *Parapanthous*, the difference between it and *Amulius* are minor only, which leads one to suppose that they are synonymous.

Phonolibinæ Miller 1952. Two genera, *Phonolibes* Stål 1854 and *Lophocephala* Laporte 1832 are contained in this subfamily; the former is distributed in the Ethiopian Region and the latter in India and Ceylon. *Phonolibes* has a somewhat elongate head, constricted immediately behind the eyes, widely separated ocelli, straight three-segmented rostrum, the articulation between the second and third segments being very feebly demarcated (a fact which has lead to the opinion that the rostrum is composed of two segments only) and no stridulatory furrow or harpagones. Abundant, short secretory hairs are usually present. *Lophocephala* has similar characters but a stridulatory furrow is present.

Phonolibes species are nocturnal and remain concealed in the daytime under logs lying on the ground. They have also been found in the nests of termites. Alary polymorphism occurs in both sexes. Dorsal glands are present in the neanides on the third, fourth and fifth segments of the abdomen. The ovum of *Phonolibes obsoletus* Horvath 1914 which is deposited singly by the female is ampulliform with a minutely granulose chorion. Nothing is known of the habits or developmental stages of *Lophocephala*.

Tegeinæ Villiers 1948. This subfamily contains four genera: *Tegea* Stål 1863, *Campylorhyncha* Stål 1870, *Tegellula* Breddin 1912 and *Nannotegea* Miller 1953, all confined to the Indo-Australian Region. The species belonging to these genera are characterized by having a straight rostrum composed of two or three segments, small eyes, small and widely separated ocelli, usually a glabrous integument, the posterior lobe of the pronotum much longer than the anterior lobe and abundant glandular setæ. The scutellum has a thick apical spine. The division between segments two and three of the rostrum is not well-defined. The prosternal furrow is somewhat obscurely striate, particularly at the middle where also the striæ are wider than those at the posterior end. In *Tegea atropicta* Stål 1863, the striæ which are particularly obscure are confined to part of the basal third of the furrow and are absent from the rest of the furrow. The rostrum in this species extends almost to the posterior margin of the mesosternum where there are somewhat indefinite transverse sulci, between which the ridges are rounded. In all genera it would seem that the rostrum is tending to become longer and the striæ in the prosternal furrow to degenerate.

The habitats of **Tegeinæ** are the trunks of forest trees. The ova and methods of oviposition are unknown. There is no information regarding their food but from the shape of the rostrum it seems likely that they search for their prey by probing crevices and borings in the bark of trees.

References
Abalos and Wygodzinsky 1951; Blanchard 1902; Brindley 1930; Brumpt 1912, 1914a 1914b; China and Usinger 1949; Costa Lima, Campos Seabra and Hathaway 1951; Jacobson 1911; Kershaw 1909 Kirkaldy 1911; Miller 1953, 1955; Readio 1926, 1927; Roepke 1932; Schouteden 1931; Shun-ichi Nakao 1954; Usinger 1943, 1944, 1946; Verhoeff 1893; Villiers 1945, 1949; Wygodzinsky 1946, 1947, 1948.

VELOCIPEDIDAE Bergroth 1891. *Wien ent. Ztg.* **10,** 265

This family contains only one genus of which four species are known at present. They are medium-sized, broadly oval insects with a long rostrum composed of three segments and with slender antennæ composed of four segments. They have prominent eyes, a wide scutellum with a distinct cuneus and wide embolium.

The females have an ovipositor and, although nothing is known of their habits and life history, it may be assumed that they insert their ova into plant tissues. Possibly not more than eight or ten ova develop at one time. The ovum of *Scotomedes alienus* (Distant) 1904 is relatively large, cylindrical, narrow, feebly curved and with a narrow differentiated portion. This species is distributed in Sikhim, Burma and Indo-China, but others yet undetermined, have been collected in Sarawak, Dutch New Guinea and in the Philippine Islands.

The relationship of the family has been discussed by several authors, including Stål, Bergroth, Distant, Kirkaldy, Reuter and Blöte; the last-mentioned considered that it is allied to the Nabidæ. This view is probably correct.

References Blöte 1945; Distant 1904.

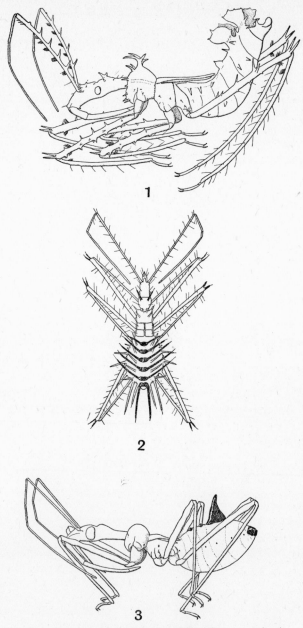

Fig. 38. Neanides of Reduviidæ (Harpactorinæ)

1. *Sphagiastes ramentaceus* (Germar) 1837. Fifth instar.
2. *Hoffmannocoris chinai* Miller 1950. First instar.
3. *Pantoleistes* sp. Fourth instar.

NABIDAE Costa 1852 *Cimic. Neap. Cent.* **3,** 66

This family is composed of mainly small or very small dull-coloured insects with predaceous habits. There are, however, certain genera which have some part of the body brightly coloured, the colours mainly red and yellow. Among those so coloured may be mentioned *Prostemma* Laporte 1832 **(Prostemminæ)**, *Aristonabis* Reuter and Poppius 1909, *Alloeorhynchus* Fieber 1861 **(Nabinæ).**

Fig. 39

Scotomedes alienus (Distant) 1904
(Velocipedidæ)

Fig. 40

Nabis ferus Linnæus 1761
(Nabidæ)

The Nabidæ are closely related to the Reduviidæ and were formerly placed in that family as a subfamily. They may be distinguished from the great majority of Reduviidæ mainly by the rostrum which has four visible segments. Most of the Nabidæ are fully alate but brachypterous forms occur in several, genera, for example in *Nabicula* Kirby 1837, *Dolichonabis* Reuter 1908, *Reduviolus* Kirby 1837, *Hoplistocelis* Reuter 1890, *Vernonia* Buchanan White 1878, *Alloeorhynchus* **(Nabinæ)** and *Prostemma.* The legs are mostly slender and setose. In *Gorpis* Stål 1859 the anterior legs are similar to an Emesine type and the males of some species of *Arbela* Stål 1865 **(Nabinæ)** have a dense tuft of setæ near the base of the posterior tibiæ. Nabidæ are found mostly on plants and some of them insert their ova into plant tissues. The ova of several species have been described. They are mostly cylindrical, somewhat slender, straight or feebly curved, with a short differentiated portion of the chorion.

Arachnocoris albomaculatus Scott 1881 (**Arachnocorinæ**) has been recorded in association with spiders.

The Nabidæ are mainly nocturnal and are often attracted to artificial light. They are universally distributed.

There are five subfamilies: **Nabinæ** Reuter 1890, with sub-membranous hemelytra; **Prostemminæ** Reuter 1890 with the corium and clavus coriaceous; **Arachnocorinæ** Reuter 1890 with the abdomen constricted basally; **Gorpinæ** Reuter 1909 with the abdomen enlarged basally; **Carthasinæ** Blatchley 1926, small and slender with the anteocular sub-cylindrical, produced and with no ocelli.

References

Carayon 1950 b; Myers 1925; Reuter and Poppius 1909; Southwood 1953.

POLYCTENIDAE Westwood 1874, *Thesaur. Ent.* 197

This family is allied to the Cimicidæ and is parasitic on bats. In general habitus the Polyctenidæ are somewhat similar to dipterous bat-parasites of the family Nycteribiidæ; in fact, the first known Polyctenid, *Polyctenes molossus* Giglioli 1864 was placed in

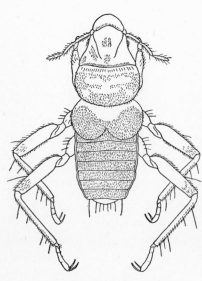

that family. Some years later Westwood proposed the family Polyctenidæ and placed it in the Order Anopleura. In 1879 Waterhouse placed the family again in the Diptera, but, a year later, he agreed (although with some doubt) to its hemipterous affinities.

The fact that the Polyctenidæ should be considered hemipterous was established by Speiser who placed it near the Cimicidæ where it now stands. With regard to reproduction, in view of the close relationship between this family and the Cimicidæ, it would not be unreasonable to infer that the methods of copulation were similar. This is not the case, however.

Fig. 41

Hesperoctenes impressus Horvath 1910
(Polyctenidæ)

In the Cimicidæ it has been demonstrated that the spermatozoa are received through a slit or emargination of the posterior margin of the fourth or fifth visible segment. The spermatozoa gradually reach the hæmocoel whence they make their way to the oviduct and the ova.

Jordan has pointed out that the intromittent organs of the males of Cimicidæ and Polyctenidæ are similar which might suggest the presence in the Polyctenidæ of an 'organ of Berlese' but he shows that the structure of the female abdomen does not indicate that copulation is effected in the manner common to the Hemiptera. More observations are essential before the problem of the method of fertilization is resolved and, in view of the habits of these insects a solution is not likely to be obtained easily. It is noteworthy that in the Polyctenidæ the early neanidal stages are passed in the body of the female.

Polyctenidæ are somewhat rare in collections, thus the probable distribution cannot be stated precisely. There is little doubt, however, that the family occurs only in tropical and sub-tropical regions.

References

Ferris and Usinger 1939; Hagen 1931; Speiser 1904; Waterhouse 1879.

CIMICIDAE Latreille 1804, *Hist. Nat. Crust. Ins.* **12**, 235

Parasitic insects with a compressed habitus and without wings. They are photophobic. They have an oval abdomen, wide head with a short rostrum, small eyes, no ocelli, hemelytra abbreviated and scale-like.

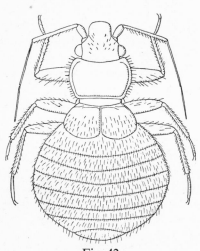

Copulation in members of this family is of a specialized type. It is effected by the male introducing the penis into a special pouch-like organ – Ribaga's organ – which has its orifice on the dorsal and ventral surface of the fourth abdominal segment, the position being a generic character. Part of the spermatozoa penetrates the walls of this pouch and, by means of the hæmocoel, reaches the *receptaculum seminis* of the female, while another part penetrates directly into the ovarioles. Yet another part is digested by the amœbal cells which group

Fig. 42

Loxaspis mirandus Rothschild 1912
(Cimicidæ)

I

around the organ, and the products of the digestion contribute eventually to the development of the ovaries which are not completely mature at the time of copulation.

In this family is the well-known bed-bug, the widely distributed human ectoparasite, *Cimex lectularius* Linnæus 1758, and many related species which are ectoparasites of birds and bats.

C. lectularius and other members of the family conceal themselves as much as possible in cracks and crevices in woodwork of houses, where they deposit their ova.

The Palæarctic Reduviid *Reduvius personatus* Linnæus 1758 is said to prey on the bed-bug, and in the Malaysian sub-Region there is evidence which, however,has not been definitely confirmed that it is attacked by another Reduviid, *Vesbius purpureus* Thunberg 1784, a small, brightly coloured species often found under the floor boards of houses of the Malay type; that is, raised on poles several feet from the ground. This Reduviid has also been seen in a concentration camp in Sumatra by the writer, where bed-bugs were present in thousands.

The ovum of *C. lectularius* is white, cylindrical, narrowed at each end and is deposited singly or in small groups.

C. lectularius, C. hemipterus Fabricius 1803, *Oeciacus hirundinis* (Jenyns) 1839 (Cimicinæ) have been recorded as vectors of *Trypanosoma cruzi*, the causative agent of Chaga's disease in South America.

The subfamilies of the Cimicidæ are: **Hæmatosiphoninæ** Jordan and Rothschild 1912, in which the bristles at the sides of the pronotum are not serrate at their outer edges and are usually cleft or dentate apically and the organ of Ribaga is usually dorsal; **Primicimicinæ** Usinger and Ferris (in press), with the clypeus narrowed apically and the rostrum very short, not extending to the level of the insertions of the antennæ; **Cimicinæ** Van Duzee 1916, with the bristles at the sides of the pronotum serrate at their outer edges and the metasternum widened posteriorly, plate-like, between the posterior coxæ; **Cacodminæ** Kirkaldy 1899, with tibiæ with fine bristles, short or long, and the organ of Ribaga usually dorsal.

References
Bacot 1921; Carayon 1953, 1954; Jordan 1922; Southall 1730; Usinger 1947 b.

ANTHOCORIDAE Fieber 1851, *Genera Hydroc.* 9

The Anthocoridæ are very small, mainly predaceous insects, some of which are cosmopolitan in range on account of their being transported from region to region in stored products such as rice and copra, among which they find their food which consists of the larvæ of coleopterous and other insect pests and of mites.

The characters of the Anthocoridæ may be summarized as follows: head produced, truncate and broadly rounded anteriorly, horizontal with the clypeus elongate, ocelli present in alate forms, antennæ with four segments, sometimes two basal segments clavate with the apical segments filiform or fusiform, pronotum usually trapeziform, convex anteriorly, depressed posteriorly, hemelytra in macropterous forms with an incomplete cuneus, membrane without basal cell and with one to four veins, male genitalia asymmetrical.

Fig. 43
Acompsocoris pygmœus
Fallen 1807
(Anthocoridæ)

Both alate and apterous forms occur but in different species. The females are sometimes provided with an ovipositor. Those with ovipositors insert their ova into vegetable tissue. Ovoviviparity occurs in some genera. Up to the present time not a great deal is known about their developmental stages or their habits, and information regarding their food, in certain instances, is based on flimsy evidence only.

The ovum of *Anthocoris confusus* Reuter 1882 (**Anthocorinæ**) according to Butler is short, cylindrical, rounded basally and apically and obliquely truncate apically. It is very pale yellow with a white collar. The ovum of *Anthocoris nemorum* Linnæus 1761 (**Anthocorinæ**) according to the same author is pale yellowish-white. It is cylindrical, rounded apically and basally and has a white collar of smaller diameter. The surface of the chorion is corrugated.

Triphleps cocciphagus Hesse 1940 (**Anthocorinæ**) has been recorded as preying on the red scale of citrus, and *Montandoniola moraguesi* Puton 1896 (**Anthocorinæ**) is predaceous on the thrips *Gnaikothrips ficorum* Marchal, a leaf-roller of *Ficus*.

Other instances of the type of food of Anthocoridæ are aphids and the pine scale *Matsucoccus* eaten by *Anthocoris nemoralis* (Fabricius) 1794 (**Anthocorinæ**), the excrement of aphids by *Anthocoris gallarum-ulmi* de Geer, ova of *Heliothis obsoleta* (Lepidoptera) devoured by *Triphleps insidiosus* Say 1831 (**Anthocorinæ**). The normal food of *Anthocoris nemorum* is apparently of an animal nature, but it has been accused of damaging leaves and shoots of the hop plant. At the same time, since it feeds on the aphids which infest that plant, the damage it causes by feeding on the plant is somewhat counterbalanced. *Lyctocoris campestris* Fabricius 1794

(**Lyctocorinæ**) has been stated to be vegetarian in its diet but later to have adopted a carnivorous diet and to feed on the blood of horses and cattle.

In Java *Triphleps* (*Orius*) *persequens* White 1877 (**Anthocorinæ**) and *Sesellius* (*Scoloposcelis*) *paralellus* Motschulsky 1863 (**Lyctocorinæ**) suck the young larvæ of *Scirpophaga* and *Proceras* (Lepidoptera).

Lasiochilus perminutus Poppius 1910 has been reported as an important enemy of the coleopterous borer of banana stems – *Cosmopolites* – (Curculionidæ). *Piezostethus flavipes* Reuter 1875, a dark brown species measuring about 2·00 mm. in length, is repeatedly found in rice and tapioca stores in Java, Sumatra and Banka. There, it most probably preys on mites and Psocids. This species is often found in holds of ships and has also been detected in stored products in various parts of the world. Anthocoridæ are also found in vegetable debris, under bark and stones, in birds' nests and burrows of mammals.

There are three subfamilies: **Lyctocorinæ** Reuter 1884, in which the cells of the metathoracic wings may have a hamus which, if present, arises from the *vena connectens*; the apical antennal segments are usually filiform; **Anthocorinæ** Reuter 1884, with the cells of the metathoracic wings always provided with a hamus which arises from the *vena decurrens* or far from it and from the *vena subtensa*, the apical antennal segments are fusiform and very rarely filiform; **Dufouriellinæ** Van Duzee 1916, in which the hamus is absent.

References

Butler 1923; Diakonoff 1941; Hesse 1940; Leston 1954 b; Poppius 1909; Reuter 1885.

MICROPHYSIDAE Dohrn 1859, *Cat. Hem.* 36

Members of this family are remarkable for the great degree of sexual dimorphism. They are very small, dull-coloured insects, apterous or alate, the former having an ovate abdomen. The antennæ have four segments and the integument is glabrous.

The Microphysidæ are rare or uncommon and, on account of their small size, can easily be overlooked by collectors. Extremely little is known of their biology with the exception of a few details concerning their habitats. They are found mainly on old and dying trees covered with moss and lichens. The females of several species are also to be found under bark, in old brushwood, under moss and in ants' nests. The males may also be found in the same sites or in vegetation in the vicinity of trees in which females are living. It is assumed that they are predaceous insects, but hardly any reliable information is available.

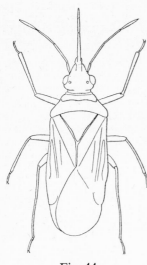

Fig. 44

Microphysa pselapiformis
Curtis 1833
(Microphysidæ)

Carayon, in an attempt to determine the food of *Myrmedobia tenella* (Zetterstedt) 1838 and of *M. coleoptrata* (Fallen) 1807, supplied females of both these species with Acarids, Collembola, Psocoptera, Thysanoptera, Psyllidæ, larval microlepidoptera, but the attempt to gain information was in vain. On the contrary, females of *Loricula elegantula* (Bærensprung) 1858 several times captured and fed on small Psocoptera especially *Reuterella helvimaculata* End., as well as *Lachesiella pedicularia* Linnæus. *Loricula* fed readily in captivity, but in the absence of prey were inclined to cannibalism.

The ovum of *Loricula elegantula*, according to Butler, is about one third of a millimetre long; short, broad, rounded posteriorly, truncate at right angles anteriorly, with dark-brown crenulate free edge.

Oviposition methods and a detailed description of the ovum of *Myrmedobia tenella* have been recorded by Carayon. The ova are placed by the female among lichens or sometimes under the cracked and slightly raised bark of small branches. They are usually deposited singly or in groups of two.

In shape they have the general form of the ova of the Cimicoidea, but are remarkable for the long chorionic processes which spread immediately after the ovum leaves the body of the female.

All the species mentioned belong to the subfamily **Microphysinæ.**

The Microphysidæ have been divided into two subfamilies; **Microphysinæ** China 1953 in which an ovipositor is present, the rostrum has apparently either three or four segments and the membrane has distinct venation in the males; **Plokiophilinæ** China 1953 in which an ovipositor is lacking and the female genital opening is transverse; the rostrum has apparently three segments and the membrane has no venation. Representatives of this subfamily have been found in spiders' webs in Cuba.

References

Carayon 1949 b; Butler 1923; China 1953 a.

MIRIDAE Hahn 1831, *Wanz. Ins.* **1**, 234

This is a large family of mostly small insects with a delicate integument, sometimes glabrous or covered with fine and easily removed pubescence. They are variously coloured but mostly pale.

The Miridæ have large eyes but no ocelli, antennæ composed of four segments and hemelytra with distinct clavus, corium and usually a large cuneus; the membrane usually has two cells. Alary polymorphism often occurs. The legs are slender, as a rule, but in some genera the femora are somewhat incrassate; the tarsi have three segments, the apical one bearing claws and arolia in most genera. The male genitalia are asymmetrical. Generally the scutellum is triangular and smooth, the most striking departures from this shape being found in the tribe Odoniellini of the subfamily **Bryocorinæ,** in the genera *Odoniella* Haglund 1895, *Pseudoniella* China and Carvalho 1951, *Parabryocoropsis* China and Carvalho 1951, *Distantiella* China 1944, *Bryocoropsis* Schumacher 1919, *Sahlbergella* Haglund 1895 and *Yangambia* Schouteden 1942.

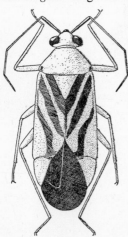

Fig. 45

Stenotus elegans
Poppius 1912
(Miridæ)

The Miridæ are mainly phytophagous; some species, however, are oligophagous and some may favour a mixed diet of plant and animal matter. Some, indeed, are mainly zoophagous, and facultative blood-sucking on human beings has been recorded. The adoption of a carnivorous habit probably has its origin in the ease in which a primitive phytophagous bug could alternate the sucking of plant sap with the piercing of small insects associated with the same host-plant.

Several of the phytophagous species are of economic importance, *e.g.*, *Sahlbergella singularis* Haglund 1895 which attacks cacao in West Africa, *Kiambura coffeæ* China 1936, a pest of the coffee plant in East Africa and *Calocoris fulvomaculatus* de Geer 1773 which damages fruit trees in Europe.

Another economically important genus is *Helopeltis* Signoret 1858 (**Bryocorinæ**) species of which cause extensive damage to tea and cinchona in India, Ceylon, Malaysia and Africa. They also feed on many other plants of various Orders, an important fact to take note of when control measures are under consideration.

Both neanides and adults of *Helopeltis* spp. attack the young leaves and shoots of the host-plants, the result being that the area around the site of the puncture turns brown and finally black. In the event of severe attack the entire leaf shrivels, and in the case of the tea plant, is useless for the manufacture of tea.

Among zoophagous species may be mentioned *Derœocoris ruber* (Linnæus) 1758 (**Phylinæ**), predaceous on aphids, *Cyrtorhinus mundulus* (Breddin) 1896 (**Orthotylinæ**), an enemy of the sugarcane pest *Perkinsiella saccharicida* Kirkaldy (Homoptera), *Stethoconus cyrtopeltis* Flor 1860 (**Phylinæ**), predaceous on *Stephanitis pyri* (Fabricius) 1803 (**Tingidæ**) and *Campyloneura virgula* (Herrich-Schaeffer) 1835 (**Phylinæ**) which feeds on Psocids. Myrmecophilous Miridæ have been recorded, for example, *Lissocapsus wasmanni* Bergroth 1903 (**Phylinæ**) which lives in the nest of *Cremastogaster ranavalonis* Forel in Madagascar.

Recently an interesting case of the association of a carnivorous Mirid, *Cyrtopeltis droseræ* China 1953 (**Phylinæ**) has been recorded. This Mirid has been found living on various species of Sundew (*Drosera*) in Western Australia. The extraordinary fact in this connexion is the ability of this species to move freely over the sticky glandular hairs of the leaves without being entangled. Their food consists of freshly captured flies.

Another Mirid, *Setocoris bybliphilus* China and Carvalho 1951 (**Phylinæ**) has been found on the insectivorous plant *Byblis gigantea* also in Western Australia. When these Mirids walk on the leaves they rarely place more than two legs at a time on the sticky parts. In this way they are able to extricate themselves by means of the remaining legs, which are placed on the parts from which the sticky substance is absent.

The ova of Miridæ are usually cylindrical and somewhat curved with a narrow differentiated portion of the chorion. Some ova have one or more slender processes through which air is able to penetrate. Examples of such ova are those of *Helopeltis* and *Megacoelum* Fieber 1858 (**Mirinæ**).

Oviposition may be on the plant (the usual method), inserted into the softer parts of the plant such as young shoots, cf. *Helopeltis* and *Cyllocoris* Hahn 1834 (**Orthotylinæ**) or between bracts. The fact that ova are inserted by the female in the young shoots is a considerable factor in control, especially in the case of tea from which those parts of the plant are systematically plucked for the preparation of the dried leaf.

Regarding eclosion, ecdysis and other incidents in the course of development of Miridæ, much information has been published on the European species, particularly by Kullenberg. This author also gives details of the various odours of the secretions, some of which, according to him, are by no means unpleasant to the human sense of smell.

There is not much information concerning the natural enemies of Miridæ. They appear to be birds, spiders and predaceous Hemiptera.

The Miridæ are divided into the following subfamilies: **Mirinæ** Reuter 1910, elongate insects with the pronotum not constricted anteriorly but carinate laterally at the anterior angles; **Orthotylinæ** Van Duzee 1916, with the arolia parallel or convergent towards the apices; usually slender; pronotal collar, if present, of the depressed type, not separated from the pronotum by a furrow; **Phylinæ** Douglas and Scott 1865 with the thorax simple and lacking an apical constriction; **Bryocorinæ** Douglas and Scott 1865, with the pseudarolia arising from the ventral surface of the claw; the membrane with one cell; the tarsi thickened towards apex; **Deræocorinæ** Douglas and Scott 1865 with opaque hemelytra the membrane of which has two cells; scutellum large and triangular; claws thickened or toothed basally; **Cylapinæ** Kirkaldy 1903 with the claws smooth basally, long and slender.

References

Bergroth 1903; Butler 1923; Carvalho 1952; China 1951, 1953; China and Carvalho 1951; Kullenberg 1944; Leston 1952; Miller 1937, 1941; Usinger 1939, 1946 b.

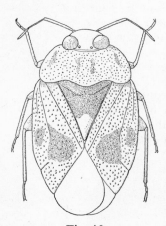

Fig. 46

Isometopus mirificus
Mulsant and Rey 1879
(Isometopidæ)

Carvalho 1951; Hesse 1947.

ISOMETOPIDAE Fieber 1860,
Wien ent. Monatschr. **4,** 259

Small flattened insects similar to Miridæ but with ocelli. They have a short head and incrassate posterior femora. They are able to jump.

Antennal structure in *Alcecoris globosus* Carvalho 1951 is remarkable in that the basal segment is thick and bears a moderately long spine and the second segment is elliptical and strongly globose.

The few known genera are distributed in the Palæarctic and Oriental Regions. Very little is known about their habits. *Letaba bedfordi* Hesse 1942, found in South Africa, is predaceous on the red scale of citrus.

References

DIPSOCORIDAE Dohrn 1859, *Cat. Hem.* 56

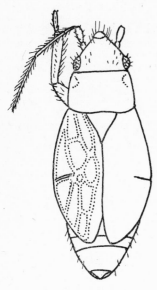

Fig. 47

Cryptostemma sordida
China 1946 (after China)
(Dipsocoridæ)

This family contains very small dark-coloured insects which live in the soil among decaying leaves, under stones or, in fact, any secluded spot that is not too dry. They are mostly nocturnal but sometimes appear in the daytime when they may be found on low vegetation and shrubs.

The site of oviposition is unknown but, judging by the habits of the adults, the ova are placed in the soil and among debris forming the usual habitat of the adult.

The only ova described so far are those extracted from dead females. They are relatively large, their length corresponding to that of the abdomen and their width indicates that not more than two ova can mature at the same time. The ornamentation of the ovum is very varied and complex.

The Dipsocoridae are widely distributed.

Reference

China 1946.

SCHIZOPTERIDAE Reuter 1891, *Acta. Soc. Sci. fenn.* **19**, 3

The Schizopteridæ formerly placed in the Dipsocoridæ as a subfamily, are minute insects characterized by the very variable structure of the hemelytra, the strongly transverse head, which is deflexed and pressed between the anterior acetabula, the short rostrum, the antennæ inserted below the eyes and by having the pronotum transversely arcuately sulcate anteriorly. Brachypterous forms occur. Representatives of the family are widely distributed. They live mainly in mosses and vegetable debris.

References

Wygodzinsky 1947 a; 1950.

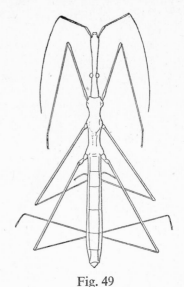

Fig. 48

Vilhenannus
angolensis
Wygodzinsky 1950
(after Wygodzinsky)
(Schizopteridæ)

Fig. 49

Hydrometra stagnorum
Linnæus 1758
(Hydrometridæ)

HYDROMETRIDAE Billberg 1820, *Enum. Ins. Mus. Billb.* 67

Long and very slender aquatic Heteroptera with long, slender legs and antennæ. The head is elongate and much longer than the thorax. Ocelli are absent. The tarsi are composed of three segments and are provided with claws.

The Hydrometridæ appear to subsist on dead prey which they find in their principal habitats, calm water and the margins of streams. There are three subfamilies: **Hydrometrinæ** Esaki 1927, **Limnobatodinæ** Esaki 1927 and **Heterocleptinæ** Villiers 1948. The first mentioned is widely distributed, the second Neotropical

---

PLATE V (*facing*)

Gerridæ; Nepidæ; Belostomatidæ; Naucoridæ

1. *Lethocerus niloticum* (Stål) 1854. Belostomatidæ.
2. *Abedus ovatus* Stål 1862. Belostomatidæ.
3. *Cheirochela feana* Montandon 1897. Naucoridæ.
4. *Limnometra femorata* Mayr 1865. Gerridæ.
5. *Cylindrostethus productus* Spinola 1840. Gerridæ.
6. *Laccotrephes fabricii* Stål 1863. Nepidæ.
7. *Ranatra elongata* (Fabricius) 1790. Nepidæ.

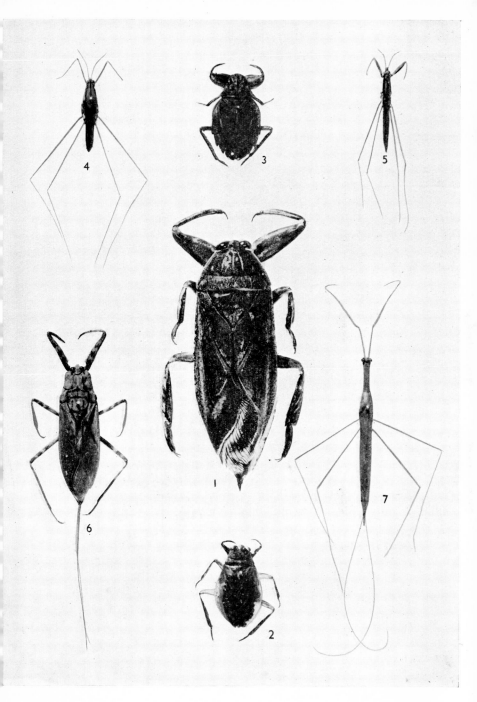

Plate V

and the last, Ethiopian. The **Hydrometrinæ** have antennæ with four segments, the metasternum without an omphalium and the claws inserted apically on the tarsi; the **Limnobatodinæ** have antennæ with five segments, the head and pronotum with short spines, the metasternum with a simple omphalium at the middle of the posterior margin and small tarsal claws inserted subapically dorsally; the **Heterocleptinæ** have antennæ with five segments, two ocellar spots behind the eyes, head and pronotum with short, fine pilosity and the metasternum with two separated omphalia on the posterior margin.

GERRIDAE Leach 1815, *Brewster's Edinb. Encyc.* IX, 123.

Small or moderately large insects living on the surface of fresh, brackish or sea water. In moving over the surface of the water they use the median and posterior legs simultaneously and are able to swim against a strong current.

The anterior legs, not of a predatory type, are used for seizing their food, which consists of living and dead organisms.

Sexual dimorphism occurs. The adults have metathoracic glands.

There are five subfamilies: **Gerrinæ** Bianchi 1896, **Halobatinæ** Bianchi 1896, **Ptilomerinæ** Esaki 1927, **Hermatobatinæ** Coutière and Martin 1901 and **Rhagadotarsinæ** Lundblad 1933. Of these the **Halobatinæ** and **Hermatobatinæ** are marine and live on floating animal matter.

The females oviposit on seaweed, floating feathers and even on the plumage of birds. Occasionally oviposition occurs on an individual of the same species.

The **Gerrinæ** have an elongate body, usually a long abdomen and moderately long antennæ. The internal margin of the eyes is concavely emarginate. The mesonotum is large. The **Halobatinæ** are small stumpy insects with the internal margin of the eyes convex. The anterior legs are thickened and the abdomen is usually small. The **Ptilomerinæ** have a cylindrical body, prominent

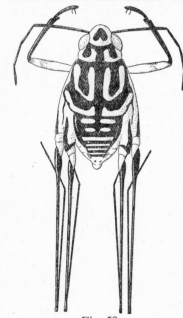

Fig. 50

Metrocoris stali Dohrn 1860
(Gerridæ)

eyes with the internal margin of the eyes distinctly emarginate, long, slender antennæ which are longer than half the length of the body. The rostrum is robust and acute. **Hermatobatinæ** have an ovate and stumpy body entirely covered with fine pubescence and the meso- and metanotum fused. **Rhagadotarsinæ** have a wide, short head, very large eyes with the internal margin not concave and long anterior femora.

The **Gerrinæ** are widely distributed. **Halobatinæ** are found in the Atlantic, Indian and Pacific Oceans, **Ptilomerinæ** in the Indo-Australian Region. **Hermatobatinæ,** in which there is one genus, are found off the coasts of Australia. **Rhagadotarsinæ** are distributed in the Oriental Region and South Ethiopian Region.

VELIIDAE Dohrn 1859, *Cat. Hem.* 53

Mostly small insects with the body widened at the level of the thorax. They have no ocelli or predatory legs. There are often two forms, one macropterous, the other apterous.

The Veliidæ are gregarious and predaceous. In movement they use only their median legs. In *Rhagovelia* Mayr 1865 **(Rhagoveliinæ)** the apical segment of the tarsus of the median legs is furcate and has a tuft of feathery setæ which spread out on the water during movement. The tarsi of *Tetraripis* Lundblad 1936 **(Rhagoveliinæ)** are notched and have plumose setæ like the median tarsi.

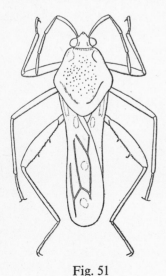

Fig. 51

Velia africana Tamanini 1946
(Veliidæ)

When Veliidæ congregate, as they do in summer, they will be seen to disperse momentarily if disturbed, but to reunite soon afterwards. The reason for such congregations is probably mutual attraction.

There are seven subfamilies of Veliidæ: **Microveliinæ** Mckinstry1942 with ocelli, hemelytra with six cellules and with a distinct metathoracic omphalium with more or less distinct lateral sulci; **Perittopinæ** China and Usinger 1949 with hemelytra containing generally four cellules and a differentiated corium; **Rhagoveliinæ** China and Usinger 1949 with the hemelytra distinctly divided into corium and membrane; the median tarsi with lamellar claws and plumose setæ; **Hebroveliinæ** Lundblad 1939, small insects resembling *Mesovelia* with antennæ and rostrum composed of four segments; membranous hemelytra with five cellules one of which along the costal margin; the tarsal claws are apical; **Microveliinæ** China and Usinger 1949 with hemelytra having four cellules and claws of the tarsi subapical; **Haloveliinæ** Esaki 1930, very small, with a thick, pubescent body; the eyes are wider than long, the antennæ shorter than the body with the basal segment thick and feebly curved; the rostrum extends to the posterior coxæ; aptery is very frequent and in individuals with this condition the mesonotum is not concealed by the pronotum; **Veliinæ** China and Usinger 1949, fairly large insects which are frequently macropterous and which have the tarsi composed of three segments. The mesonotum is partly covered by the pronotum in apterous forms.

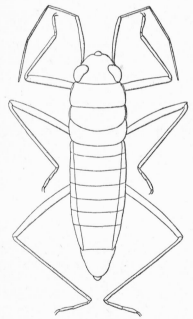

Fig. 52
Mesovelia furcata Mulsant and Rey 1852
(Mesoveliidæ)

MESOVELIIDAE
Douglas and Scott 1867
Ent. Mon. Mag. **4,** 3

Small, slender macropterous or apterous insects of dull colouration. They have a wide head with large eyes and ocelli, a long rostrum and long, slender antennæ. The tarsi have three segments, claws but no arolia.

As regards habitat, they prefer pieces of smooth water with an abundant vegetation among which they feed on dead and feeble organisms.

The females insert their ova into vegetable tissue. A cavernicolous and halophilous species, *Speovelia maritima* Esaki 1929, has been found in Japan living on the walls of a cave communicating with the sea.

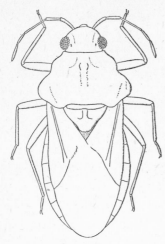

Fig. 53

Hebrus pusillus Fallen 1807
(Hebridæ)

HEBRIDAE Fieber 1851

Genera Hydroc. 9

Very small aquatic insects with a short, thick body, large eyes, ocelli, a long rostrum which lies in a ventral sulcus when not in use, antennæ composed of four or five segments, a small scutellum, hemelytra with the corium with one cell and the clavus membranous. The membrane is wide and without nervures. The legs are short and robust and similar to each other. Odoriferous glands are present. The Hebridæ live in swamps and on moss on banks of streams. They are distributed in the Palæarctic, Nearctic, Neotropical, Ethiopian and Oriental Regions.

LEOTICHIIDAE China, 1933 *Ann. Mag. nat. Hist.* (10) **12,** 185

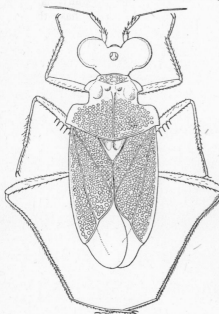

Fig. 54

Leotichius speluncarum China 1941
(Leotichiidæ)

This family contains a single genus *Leotichius* Distant 1904 which is found, so far as is known, only in the Indo-Malayan Region.

It is allied to the Leptopodidæ but it differs principally in having the rostrum without spines, short antennæ of which the basal and second segments are thick, a carinate pronotum, the anterior tarsi with one segment and the remaining tarsi with two segments. One species, *Leotichius speluncarum* China 1941 has been found on bat guano in limestone caves in Malaya and *L. glaucopis* Distant 1904 in caves in Burma.

Fig. 55

Leptopus marmoratus
Horvath 1897
(Leptopodidæ)

LEPTOPODIDAE Costa 1838
Cimic. Reg. Neap. **1**, 151

Small, dull-coloured insects allied to the Saldidæ. They are characterized by the short rostrum, the basal segment of which (or sometimes segments one and two) is spinose, by prominent ocelli, subpedunculate eyes, incrassate anterior femora and tibiæ armed with long, slender spines.

So far as is known, Leptopodidæ are confined almost entirely to the tropical and sub-tropical regions of the eastern hemisphere, but do not appear to be abundant, possibly because they are overlooked on account of their small size. Little is known about their ecology. Neanides have only one abdominal scent gland, the ostiole of which is located between segments three and four.

SALDIDAE Costa 1852, *Cimic. Reg. Neap.* **3**, 66

Generally dark-coloured, soft-bodied insects found in proximity to fresh-water streams. They probably feed on insect remains and dipterous larvæ, but this is uncertain.

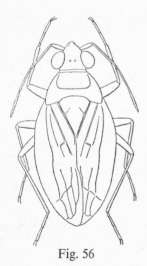

Fig. 56

Salda littoralis Linnæus 1758
(Saldidæ)

Saldidæ are mostly oval shaped with a short, wide head and prominent eyes. The antennæ are long, also the rostrum which does not lie on the ventral surface of the head when not in use.

Neanides have one abdominal scent gland the ostiole of which is situated between segments three and four. Certain species are halophilous. When disturbed they jump and fly off.

The Saldidæ have been considered to be the most primitive of living Heteroptera, in respect of their short gular area, the ventrally directed mouth, their primitive feeding habits, habitat and methods of oviposition. This opinion, however, has not been generally accepted. The Saldidæ appear to be confined to the Palæarctic and Nearctic Regions.

References Ekblom 1926; Spooner 1938.

AEPOPHILIDAE Puton 1879, *Syn. Hém. Het. France*, **2**, 145

This family contains one genus and one species, *Aepophilus bonnairei* Signoret 1879. It is a small, ovate, delicate insect, pubescent and with small eyes and no ocelli. The hemelytra are reduced to triangular scales, pointed apically.

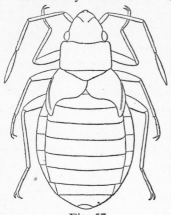

Aepophilus appears to be related to the Saldidæ and lives on the shore at the tidal zone, concealing itself under deeply embedded stones at high tide. When the tide is low it moves about on stranded seaweed and is often found in association with Coleoptera. The neanides are gregarious. They have only one abdominal scent gland, the ostiole of which is situated between segments three and four.

Fig. 57

Aepophilus bonnairei Signoret 1897
(Aepophilidæ)

Reference: Bergroth 1899.

NOTONECTIDAE Leach 1815, *Brewster's Edinb. Encyc.* **9**, 124

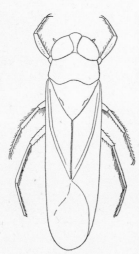

The Notonectidæ are characterized by the large reniform eyes, lack of ocelli, antennæ with three or four segments, a short rostrum composed of four segments, a large triangular scutellum, hemelytra without venation and posterior legs formed for swimming. Odoriferous glands are present.

Larger species of Notonectidæ attack the fry of fish, young batrachians, while smaller species and neanides attack small crustacea. The males are able to stridulate.

The female, when ovipositing, either inserts the ova into vegetable tissue or affixes them to a plant-stem or other object.

There are two subfamilies: **Anisopinæ** Hutchinson 1929, with a foveole on the clavus behind the apex of the scutellum, and **Notonectinæ** Fieber 1860 without such a foveole. The males of **Anisopinæ** have stridulatory organs. The Notonectidæ are widely distributed.

Fig. 58

Anisops sardea
Herrich-Schaeffer 1849
(Notonectidæ)

Reference Walton 1936.

PLEIDAE Fieber 1851 *Genera Hydroc.* 27

Small insects which are remarkable in having the head and prothorax partially fused. They have a strongly convex body, rostrum composed of four segments and the antennæ with three segments. The legs are formed for locomotion.

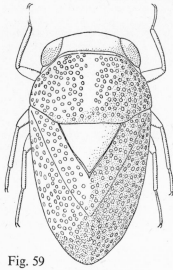

The habitat of Pleidæ is principally the still waters of ponds and lakes where they live among aquatic vegetation. They swim on the back and propel themselves by the posterior legs, the tibiæ and tarsi of which have two rows of setæ. They move from place to place often by clinging to floating vegetation. The females insert their ova into plant material. The Pleidæ are to be found in the Palæarctic, Oriental, Australian, Nearctic and Neotropical Regions.

Fig. 59

Plea pullula Stål 1855
(Pleidæ)

HELOTREPHIDAE Esaki and China 1927, *Trans. R. ent. Soc. Lond.* 280

The Helotrephidæ are allied to the Pleidæ which they resemble in having the head and pronotum fused. They have antennæ with three segments, a long scutellum and the genital segments of the male twisted to the left. The tarsi have spiniform arolia and a tubular membranous empodium. Very little is known about their ecology.

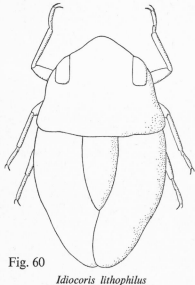

There are three subfamilies: **Neotrephinæ** China 1940 with the scutellum much longer than wide; **Idiocorinæ** Esaki and China 1927 with a flattened body, no suture between the head and pronotum; **Helotrephinæ** Esaki and China 1927 with a strongly convex body and a suture between the head and pronotum. The Helotrephidæ are distributed in the Neotropical, Ethiopian, Mascarene and Oriental Regions.

Fig. 60

Idiocoris lithophilus
Esaki and China 1927
(Helotrephidæ)

CORIXIDAE Leach 1815, *Brewster's Edinburgh Encyclopædia* **9**, 124

Moderately large or small aquatic insects usually dull in colour with the pronotum and hemelytra sometimes with a linear or vermiculate pattern. The very mobile and wide head has large eyes and a large, apparently unsegmented rostrum. The hemelytra and wings are well-developed. Scent glands are present in the neanides on the third, fourth and fifth segments of the abdomen. In the adult the glands are found on the metathorax with the ostioles at the sides of the median coxæ.

The anterior legs are short with the apical segment generally flattened and margined with robust setæ. The median legs are long and slender and the posterior legs have robust femora, short tibiæ and flattened tarsi with marginal setæ. Each leg is adapted to a particular function: the anterior legs for collecting food, the median legs for supporting the animal when stationary and the posterior legs for swimming. Corixidæ swim with the ventral surface below. They are not confined to fresh water but also occur in brackish water.

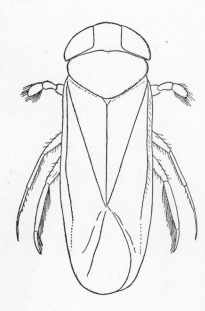

Fig. 61

Sigara pectoralis Fieber 1851
(Corixidæ)

In order to breathe, the Corixid applies the side of the thorax to the surface of the water and by repeatedly bending its head drives air into the cavities situated between the head and prosternum and between the pro- and mesosternum. Finally, the air thus entrapped reaches the abdominal spiracles and the trachaeal system.

They are largely phytophagous, a fact which refutes a common assumption that all aquatic bugs, including those belonging to this family, are predaceous. Some species prefer waters in which there is a flourishing vegetation, while others prefer areas in which the vegetation is scanty. Breeding takes place sometimes in permanent water, sometimes in temporary pools.

The food of Corixidæ, according to Hungerford, is derived from the organic ooze on the bottom of a pond or lake. In gathering it, they ingest other matter such as unicellular algæ, filaments of *Oscillatoria, Zygnema, Mougeotia* and *Spirogyra* from which they suck the chlorophyll. In their food habits they have an advantage over all other families of strictly predaceous aquatic Heteroptera on account of the continued abundance of the food supply. While many species use the modified anterior tarsi or palæ for gathering their food, there are indeed Corixidæ in which these appendages are not modified, which suggests that they live by predation.

Copulation takes place in the water and the ova are usually deposited on some submerged part of an aquatic plant, but a departure from this mode of oviposition is exhibited by the American species, *Ramphocorixa balanodis* Abbott 1912 (**Corixinæ**) an inhabitant of muddy ponds. This species has been recorded as ovipositing on the carapace of a crayfish, *Cambarus immunis* Hagen, but whether this is the sole site chosen by the females on every occasion seems open to doubt. So far as is known, most Corixid ova are more or less oval with the apex sometimes sub-acutely conical, with or without a short pedicel. The structure of Corixid ova has been described by Poisson. At the time of eclosion the embryo ruptures the apex of the chorion.

The genus *Corixa* possesses stridulatory organs. The Corixidæ generally have well-developed wings, but in some genera, namely *Palmacorixa* Abbott, *Krizousacorixa* Hungerford 1930 (**Corixinæ**) and *Cymatia* Flor 1860 (**Cymatinæ**), the metathoracic wings are often reduced and non-functional. Two abundant species in Mexico, *Corixa mercenaria* Say 1931 and *Krizousacorixa femorata* (Hungerford) 1948 (**Corixinæ**) are collected and exported for food for songbirds, poultry and fish. The ova are collected by natives who make a kind of bread from them.

The Corixidæ which are distributed throughout all zoogeographical regions are divided into six subfamilies: **Micronectinæ** Jaczewski 1924 with no ocelli, a small scutellum and antennæ with three segments; **Diaprepocorinæ** Lundblad 1928 with a single genus having two ocelli and antennæ with four segments; **Corixinæ** Douglas and Scott 1865 which have no ocelli and the scutellum concealed by the pronotum; **Stenocorixinæ** Hungerford 1948 in which the scutellum is concealed by the pronotum (rarely with the apex visible) and the hemelytra have no embolar groove; **Cymatiinæ** Walton 1940 in which the scutellum is concealed by the pronotum, the hemelytra have no embolar groove and the rostrum has no transverse sulci; the nodal furrow is absent and vein M of the hemelytra seems to curve abruptly downward to the costal margin;

Heterocorixinæ Hungerford 1948 which have the scutellum concealed by the pronotum, the rostrum with transverse sulci, a complete nodal furrow, vein M usually curving upward to fuse with Cu at or just before the origin of the nodal furrow; the infraocular portion of the genæ is very broad, the lower margin of the eye concave and vein M indistinct parallel and very near to Cu.

References

Abbott 1912; Banks 1938; Frost and Macan 1948; Hungerford 1923, 1948; Kirkaldy 1901; Mitis 1935.

NEPIDAE Latreille 1802, *Hist. Nat. Crust. Ins.* **3.** 252

(Plate 5)

Moderately large or large insects, elongate or flattened with raptorial legs. They have a small head, more or less horizontal with prominent globular eyes, a short rostrum composed of three segments directed outwards and forwards. The antennæ have three segments. All the tarsi have one segment. The neanides have no glandular ostioles and odoriferous glands appear to be absent from the adults.

Nepidæ inhabit ponds and pools on the bottom of which they crawl, or they climb on aquatic plants. The ova are provided with long respiratory processes and are inserted by the female into vegetable matter. In common with certain other insects Nepidæ exhibit the strange phenomenon of catalepsy, when they assume a completely rigid posture and hold the anterior legs straight in front and the other legs pressed close to the body. Nepidæ prey on other Arthropods.

There are two subfamilies: **Nepinæ** Douglas and Scott 1865 with an ovate and flattened body and the tibia and tarsus together as long as the anterior femora; **Ranatrinæ** Douglas and Scott 1865 with an elongate body which is almost cylindrical. The anterior tibia and tarsus are less than half as long as the femur. Although the Nepidæ are widely distributed, the majority of species is found in the Oriental, Ethiopian and Neotropical Regions.

BELOSTOMATIDAE Leach 1815

Brewster's Edinburgh Encyclopædia, **9,** 23 (Plate 5)

This family contains very large to fairly small aquatic and predaceous insects. They are somewhat flattened dorsally and convex ventrally. The abdomen is terminated by two retractile appendages formed from the eighth segment which, when joined serve as a respiratory siphon. The anterior trochanters, femora, tibiæ and tarsi have very dense, short setæ on the under surface. This setal clothing is also present on the remaining legs but is not equally dense. The median and posterior legs have a double fringe of fine and mostly long setæ. The rostrum is robust and the antennæ have four segments.

Some of the largest Heteroptera are to be found in this family, namely *Belostoma* Latreille 1807, *Lethocerus* Mayr 1852 and *Hydrocyrius* Spinola 1850. Although aquatic, representatives of the Belostomatidæ often fly from one pond or lake to another and during flight are frequently attracted to artificial light.

The Belostomatidæ are very voracious feeders and attack small fish, immature batrachians and molluscs. There is one recorded instance of a fairly large bird being attacked by *Hydrocyrius columbiæ* Spinola 1850, the bird being a Siberian ringed plover. It was found with the bug under its wing and was in a moribund condition. It was eventually killed for examination which revealed that the bug had been feeding on its liver.

Females oviposit either on vegetation or on the backs of males. The species which have been recorded as ovipositing on the males belong to the genera *Abedus* Stål 1862, *Belostoma, Sphærodema* Laporte 1832, *Poissonia* Brown 1948 and *Hydrocyrius,* but whether this method of oviposition is invariable has yet to be confirmed; also whether it is always the male and not another female which is a recipient of the ova.

Lethocerus indicum (Lepeletier and Serville) 1825 places its ova on vegetation in groups of several hundreds sometimes. This species is eaten by the Laos people of Indo-China. The Belostomatidæ are widely distributed.

References

Game Dept., Uganda 1949; Severin and Severin 1910,

NAUCORIDAE Fallen 1814, *Spec. Nov. Disp. Meth.* 3 and 5

(Plate 5)

Moderately large aquatic insects of ovate shape with a short rostrum and the elytral membrane without nervures. The anterior legs are raptorial. Many species exhibit alary polymorphism. They swim freely but often congregate among aquatic vegetation. The adults are able to stridulate and are also able to eject fluid from the rectum when disturbed. Their bite is painful.

Aphelochirus æstivalis (Fabricius) 1803 frequents running water in which stones and aquatic plants are found. It lives under them and to them the female attaches its ova.

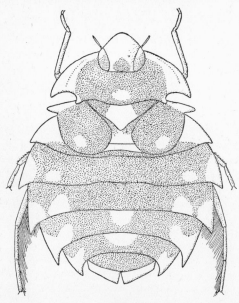

Fig. 62
Aphelocheirus variegatus Kiritschenko 1925
(Naucoridæ)

The family is divided into eight subfamilies: Naucorinæ Stål 1876, Limnocorinæ Stål 1876, Laccocorinæ Stål 1876, Cryphocricinæ Montandon 1897, Ambrysinæ Usinger, 1941, Cheirochelinæ Montandon 1897, Potamocorinæ Usinger 1941, Aphelocheirinæ Douglas and Scott 1865.

Naucorinæ Stål 1876 with the anterior tarsi composed of one segment. The anterior margin of the pronotum is straight at the middle or feebly convex behind the interocular region. The internal margin of the eyes converges anteriorly. The gula is moderately long and carinate, the meso- and metasternum not, or feebly, carinate foveolate.

Limnocorinæ Stål 1876 with the anterior tarsi having one segment. The pronotum and gula are similar to those of the Naucorinæ but the internal margin of the eyes diverges anteriorly; the meso- and metasternum are strongly carinate with the apex deeply foveolate or broadly sulcate.

Laccocorinæ Stål 1876 with the anterior tarsi composed of three segments. The pronotum as in Naucorinæ. The gula is short and non-carinate. Mesosternum with a feeble and more or less conical elevation.

Cryphocricinæ Montandon 1897, with a flattened body and the rostrum articulated to the anterior margin of the head. Labrum well-developed. Head retracted into the prothorax. Sternites of the abdomen not pubescent. Members of this subfamily are usually brachypterous.

Ambrysinæ Usinger 1941. Anterior margin of the pronotum as in Cryphocricinæ. The body is ovate and the abdominal sternites densely pubescent. The rostrum is short and articulated to the anterior margin of the head. The carina on the gula and prosternum are of equal height.

Cheirochelinæ Montandon 1897. Anterior margin of the pronotum as in Cryphocricinæ. Rostrum short and articulated to the posterior portion of a deep excavation under the head and moderately widely spaced from the anterior margin of the vertex. Labrum not visible.

Potamocorinæ Usinger 1941. Very small, primitive Naucoridæ doubtless allied to the Helotrephidæ. The head is not deeply retracted into the prothorax and the rostrum composed of three segments is slender. The antennæ are slender and composed of four segments. The gula is long and not carinate. The posterior margin of the pronotum is medially excavate. The anterior tarsi have one segment and the remaining tarsi two segments. All are armed with two claws.

Aphelocheirinæ Douglas and Scott 1865 with the legs somewhat modified for raptorial purposes, the antennæ fairly long and slender, the head triangular and the rostrum very long, slender and extending beyond the median coxæ. In the male the genital segments are asymmetrical.

The distribution of the Naucoridæ is world-wide.

GELASTOCORIDAE Kirkaldy 1897. *Entomologist* 30, 258.

Species belonging to this family are usually considered to be semi-aquatic since not only water but wet mud and vegetable debris have been noted as habitats.

The characters of representatives of this family are the somewhat batrachian-like appearance and manner, prominent eyes, raptorial anterior legs (but not strictly of the true raptorial type), antennæ with four segments concealed below the eyes. Ocelli present. Rostrum short. The male genital segments are asymmetrical. The dorsal surface of the thorax and hemelytra is often rugose.

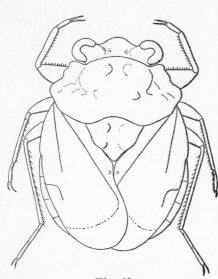

Fig. 63
Gelastocoris bufo Herrich-Schæffer 1837
(Galgulidæ)

Some species occur in stagnant water. *Mononyx nepæformis* (Fabricius) 1794 (**Mononyxinæ**) has been discovered among vegetable debris and has also been observed climbing low vegetation presumably in order to find food which appears to be small soft-bodied insects including possibly termites. This species has been seen to feign death when disturbed. *Mononyx montandoni* Melin 1930 has been found in the wet mud of rice seedbeds.

The life history of *Gelastocoris oculatus* (Fabricius) 1798 (**Galgulinæ**) in the United States of America has been described by Hungerford. This species is found on muddy banks of streams or on sandy river beaches. It has the habit of burrowing in the sand or mud, probably for the purpose of avoiding being washed away in times of flood. Any kind of insect of suitable size appears to be acceptable to them as prey.

The females oviposit either on or in sand or mud and produce about two hundred ova during the season.

The ovum is broadly oval with the chorion granular and reticulate. On eclosion it splits lengthwise for part of its length. It is not known whether an egg-burster is present.

There are two sub-families: **Galgulinæ** Billberg 1820 with the anterior tarsi provided with two claws and with the hemelytra distinctly divided into corium and membrane; **Mononyxinæ** Fieber 1851 with the tarsi armed with a single claw and the hemelytra entirely sclerotized with non-differentiated membrane.

The family is confined mostly to tropical and sub-tropical regions and occurs in North Central and South America from the United States to the Argentine and also in the West Indies, Australia, Malaysia, China, India and the Ethiopian Region.

References Hungerford 1922; Kevan 1942.

PELOGONIIDAE Leach 1815

Brewster's Edinburgh Encyclopædia, **9**, 123

Apparently semi-aquatic insects with a short, stumpy, ovate body the dorsal surface of which is pubescent. The rostrum is very long and robust. The hemelytral membrane has large, pentagonal cells in two series. Ocelli are present.

Judging by the mouthparts and the anterior legs which are of a simple type, it would seem that the Pelogoniidæ are phytophagous.

Observations on *Ochterus marginatus* Latreille 1807 show that the adults live on the shady shores of ponds and streams. They do not enter the water except by accident; but, on the other hand, the neanides are amphibious and often submerge themselves. The neanides cover their dorsum with sandy granules and when about to moult they construct small cells in the sand into which they retire until ecdysis is complete.

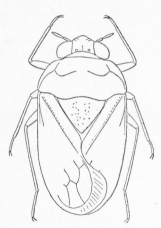

Fig. 64
Ochterus marginatus Latreille 1807
(Pelogonidæ)

When the neanides are submerged they maintain their bodies just under the surface film of the water. Before submersion they collect air on the ventral surface of the abdomen and when a fresh supply is required they rapidly turn over on their backs to expose the abdomen.

When about to copulate the male grasps the female with the second pair of legs, the anterior pair being fixed beneath the body and the abdomen somewhat to the left side. The reason for this fixed position is that the male genitalia are asymmetrical.

According to observations copulation is frequent and pairs may remain *in coitu* for as long as seven hours.

All stages are predaceous. The genus *Ochterus* Latreille 1807 is cosmopolitan and *Megochterus* Jaczewski 1933 is Australian.

Reference

Takahashi 1921.

REFERENCES

Abalos J. W. and Wygodzinsky P. 1951, *Las Triatominœ Argentinas (Reduviidœ-Hemiptera)*. Monog. 2, Instituto de Medicina Regional, Tucuman.

Abbott J. F. 1912, *Rhamphocorixa balanodis* Abbott. *Amer. Nat.* **46**, 553-5.

Amyot C. J. B. and Serville A. 1843, *Hist. Nat. Hémiptères* (suites de Buffon).

Bacot A. 1921, 'Bionomics of *Cimex hirundinis*'. *Proc. R. ent. Soc. Lond.* 2.

Balduf, W. V. 1939, 'Food Habits of *Phymata pennsylvanica americana* Melin, (Hemiptera)'. *Canad. Ent.* **71**, 66-74.

Balduf W. V. 1941, 'Life History of *Phymata pennsylvanica americana* Melin'. *Ann. ent. Soc. Amer.* **34**, 204-14.

Banks C. J. 1938, 'On the occurence of nematodes in *Corixa geoffroi* Leach (Hem-Corixidæ)'. *J. Soc. Brit. Ent.* 217-9.

Barber G. W. 1923, 'Notes on a New Zealand Aradid (*Aradus 4-lineatus*)'. *Psyche, Camb., Mass.* **30**, 120-2.

Beament J. W. L. 1946, 'The formation and structure of the chorion of the egg in an Hemipteran, *Rhodnius prolixus*'. *Quart. J. micr. Sci.* **87**, 393-439.

Beament J. W. L. 1947, 'The formation and structure of the micropylar complex in the egg-shell of *Rhodnius prolixus* Stahl (*sic*) Heteroptera-Reduviidæ'. *J. exp. Biol.* **23**, 213-33.

Bergroth E. 1886, 'Zur kenntnis der Aradiden'. *Verh. zool.-Bot. Ges. Wien* **36**, 53-60.

Bergroth E. 1892, 'Aradidi dell'isola di Engano raccolti dal Dott. Elio Modigliani'. *Ann. Mus. Stor. nat. Genova* (2), **12**, 806-8.

Bergroth E. 1899, 'Note on the genus *Aepophilus* Sign'. *Ent. month. Mag.* **35**, 282.

Bergroth E. 1903, 'Neue myrmecophile Hemipteren'. *Wien ent. Ztg.* **22**, 255-6.

Bergroth E. 1914, 'On an Hemipterous insect from an Australian opossum's nest'. *Trans. roy. Soc. S. Aust.* **38**, 53-57.

Berlese A. 1914, *Gli Insetti* **2**, fasc. 7-8, 220.

Blanchard R. 1902, 'Sur la piqure de quelques Hémiptères'. *Arch. Parasit. Paris* **5**, 1, 139-48.

Blöte H. C. 1945, 'On the systematic position of *Scotomedes* (Heteroptera-Nabidæ)'. *Zoöl. Meded.* **24**, 321-4.

Bodenheimer F. S. 1951, *Insects as human food*.

Bolivar J. 1894, *Feuill. jeun. Nat.* **24**, 43.

Brien P. 1930, 'Notes sur *Phloea paradoxa* Burm. in *Mission Biologique belge au Brèsil* (1922-23), 2, 203-12.

Haviland Brindley M. D. 1930, 'On the metasternal scent-glands of certain Heteroptera'. *Trans. R. ent. Soc. London.* **78**, 199-200.

Brues Charles T., Melander A. L., Carpenter Frank M. 1954, 'Classification of Insects'. *Bull. Mus. comp. Zool. Harv.* 108.

Brumpt E. 1912, 'Le trypanosome *cruzi* évolue chez *Conorhinus megistus*, *Cimex lectularius*, *Cimex boueti* et *Ornithodorus moubata*, cycle évolutif de ce parasite'. *Bull. Soc. Pat. exot.* **5**, 360.

Brumpt E. 1914 a, 'Importance du cannibalisme et de la coprophagie chez les Réduvidés hématophages (*Rhodnius, Triatoma*) pour la conservation des Trypanosomes pathogènes en dehors de l'hote vertèbré'. *Bull. Soc. Pat. exot.* **7**, 702-5.

Brumpt E. 1914 b, 'Le Xénodiagnostic. Application diagnostic de quelques infections parasitaires et en particulier à la trypanosome de Chagas'. *Bull. Soc. Pat. exot.* **7**, 706.

de la Torre Bueno 1935, 'Biological Notes on Aradidæ'. *Bull. Brooklyn ent. Soc.* **30**, 3, 113.

Butler E. A. 1923, *A Biology of the British Hemiptera*.

Carayon J. 1949 a, 'L'oothèque des Hémiptères Plataspidés de l'Afrique tropicale'. *Bull. Soc. ent. Fr.* **54**, 66.

Carayon J. 1949 b, 'Observations sur la Biologie des Hémiptères Microphysidés'. *Bull. Mus. Paris.* 2e serie **21**, 710-16.

Carayon J. 1950 a, 'Observations sur l'Accouplement. la Ponte et l'Eclosion chez des Hémiptères Hénicocéphalidés de l'Afrique tropicale'. *Bull. Mus. Paris* 2e serie, **22**, 6.

Carayon J. 1950 b, 'Caractères anatomiques et position systematique des Hémiptères Nabidæ (note preliminaire)'. *Bull. Mus. Paris* 2e serie, **22**, 95-101.

Carayon J. 1953, 'Organ de Ribaga et Fécondation chez un Hémiptère Cimicidé du Cambodge: *Aphraniola orientalis* Ferris and Usinger'. *Rev. Fr. Ent.* **20**, 139-45.

Carayon J. 1954, 'Fecondation hémocœlienne chez un Hémiptère Cimicidé dépourvu d'organe de Ribaga'. *C. R. Acad. Sci.* **239**, 1542-4.

Carvalho J. C. M. 1951, 'New genera and Species of Isometopidæ in the Collection of the British Museum of Natural History (Hemiptera)'. *Ann. Acad. bras. Sci.* **23**, 390.

Carvalho J. C. M. 1952, 'On the major Classification of the Miridæ (Hemiptera). (With keys to the subfamilies and tribes and a Catalogue of the World Genera)'. *Ann. Acad. bras. Sci.* **24**, 1, 31-111.

Champion G. C. 1898, *Biologia Centrali Americana, Hem-Het.* 2, 231.

China W. E. 1931, 'Morphological Parallelism in the Structure of the labium in the Hemipterous genera *Coptosomides* gen. nov. and *Bozius* Distant (Fam. Plataspidæ) in connection with mycetophagous habits'. *Ann. Mag. nat. Hist.* (10), 7, 281.

China W. E. 1933, 'A New Family of Hemiptera-Heteroptera with notes on the phylogeny of the suborder'. *Ann. Mag. nat. Hist.* (10), 12, 180-96.

China W. E. 1943. The Generic Names of British Insects **8**. Hemiptera-Heteroptera. 217-325.

China W. E. 1946, 'New Cryptostemmatidæ (Hemiptera) from Trinidad, British West Indies'. *Proc. R. ent. Soc. Lond.* Ser. B **15**, 148-54.

China W. E. 1953 a, 'A new subfamily of Microphysidæ (Hemiptera-Heteroptera). *Ann. Mag. nat. Hist.* (12), 6, 67.

China W. E. 1953 b, 'Two new species of the genus *Cyrtopeltis* (Hemiptera) associated with sundews in Western Australia'. *W. Aust. Nat.* **4**, 1, 1-12.

China W. E. 1954, 'Notes on the nomenclature of the Pyrrhocoridæ (Hemiptera-Heteroptera)'. *Ent. mon. Mag.* **90**, 188.

China W. E. 1955a, 'A Reconsideration of the Classification of the Joppeicidæ with Notes on the Phylogeny of the Heteroptera'. *Ann. Mag. nat. Hist.* (12) 8, 257-67, (12) 8, 353-70.

China W. E. 1955b, 'The Evolution of the Waterbugs' *Nat. Inst. Sci. India Bull.* VII, 91-103.

China W. E. and Carvalho J. C. M. 1951, 'A new Ant-like Mirid from Western Australia (Hemiptera-Miridæ)'. *Ann. Mag. nat. Hist.* (12) 4, 221.

China W. E. and Miller N. C. E. 1955, 'Check List of Family and Subfamily names of the Hemiptera-Heteroptera'. *Ann. Mag. nat. Hist.*

China W. E. and Usinger R.L. 1949, 'A New Genus of Tribelocephalinæ from Fernando Poo (Hemiptera-Reduviidae)'. *Ann. Mus. Stor. nat. Genova* **64**, 43-7.

Conradi Albert F. 1904, 'Variations in the protective value of the odoriferous secretions of some Heteroptera'. *Science* (n.s.) **19**, 393-4.

Cook A. J. 1879, 'Another Bee Enemy'. *Canad. Ent.* **11**, 17-20.

Corby H. D. L. 1947, '*Aphanus* (Hem.-Lygæidæ) in Stored Groundnuts'. *Bull. ent. Res.* **37**, 609-617.

Corbett G. H. and Miller N. C. E. 1933, 'A List of Insects with their Parasites and Predators in Malaya'. *Sci. Ser. Dept. Agric. S.S. and F.M.S.* 13.

Costa Lima A. da. 1940, *Insetos do Brasil.* 2.

Costa Lima A. da., Campos C. A., Hathaway C. R. 1951, 'Estudo dos Apiomeros'. *Mem. Inst. Osw. Cruz* **49**, 273-442.

Cott H. B. 1934, 'The Zoological Society's Expedition to the Zambesi 1947, No. 5. On a collection of Lizards from Portuguese East Africa with descriptions of new species of *Zonarus*, *Monopeltis* and *Chirindea*'. *Proc. zool. Soc. Lond.* 145-73.
Cuthbertson A. 1934, 'Note on the swarming of Pentatomid Bugs'. *Nada* Ann. Native Affairs Dept. S. Rhodesia. 38.
Dahms R. G. and Kagan M. 1938, 'Egg parasite of the Cinch Bug'. *J. econ. Ent.* 31, 799-780.
Deventer W. van 1906, 'De Dierlijke vijanden van het Suikerriet en hunne Parasieten'. *Handboek te Dienst van de Suikerreit-Cultuur in de Rietsuiker-Fabricage op Java* 2 deel.
Diakonoff A. 1941, *Arch. Suikerind Ned-Ind.* 2, 205-13.
Distant W. L. 1903, *Fasc. Malay* 2.
Distant W. L. 1904, *The Fauna of British India* (*Rhynchota*), 2.
Dodd F. P. 1904, 'Notes on Maternal Instinct in Rhynchota'. *Trans. R. ent. Soc. Lond.* 483-6.
Douglas J. W. and Scott J. 1865, *The British Hemiptera.*
Dufour L. 1833, 'Recherches anatomiques et physiologiques sur les Hémiptères etc'. *Mem. des Savants étrang. à l'Academie des Sciences* 4, 129-462.
Dufour L. 1834, 'Observations sur le genre *Prostemma*.' *Ann. Soc. ent. Fr.* 3, 350.

Ekblom Tore 1926, 'Morphological and Biological Studies of the Swedish Families of Hemiptera-Heteroptera'. *Zool. Bidr. Uppsala* 10.
Esaki R. and Matsuda R. 1951, 'Hemiptera Micronesica, 3, Dysodiidæ'. *Mushi* 22, 73-86.
Evans J. W. 1948, *Insect Pests and their Control* Tasmanian Department of Agriculture.

Ferris G. F. and Usinger R. L. 1939, 'The Family Polyctenidæ (Hemiptera-Heteroptera)'. *Microentomology* 4, 1, 1-50.
Frost W. E. and Macan T. T. 1948, 'Corixidæ as food of Fish'. *J. Anim. Ecol.* 174-9.

'Game Department of Uganda, Report'. 1949. Quoted in *Oryx* 1, No. 2 1951.
Gillett J. D. and Wigglesworth V. B. 1932, 'The Climbing Organ of an Insect, *Rhodnius prolixus* (Hemiptera-Reduviidæ'. *Proc. roy. Soc. B.* 111, 365-75.
Girault A. A. 1906, 'Standards of the numbers of eggs laid by insects'. *Ent. News.* 17, 6.
Grandi, G. 1951, *Introd. Stud. Ent.* 1, 337.
Gross J. 1901, 'Untersuchungen über das Ovarium der Hemipteren zugleich ein Betrag zur Amitosenfrage'. *Z. wiss. Zool.* 69, 139-201.

Hagen H. R. 1931, 'The Embryogeny of the Polyctenid *Hesperoctenes fumarius* Westwood with reference to viviparity in insects'. *J. Morph.* 51, 1-92.
Handlirsch A. 1900 a, 'Zur Kenntnis der Stridulationsorgane bei den Rhyncoten'. *Ann. Nat. Hofm. Wien.* 15, 127-41.
Handlirsch A. 1900 b, 'Neue Beitrage zur Kenntnis der Stridulationsorgane bei den Rhyncoten'. *Verh. zool.-bot. Ges. Wien* 50, 555-60.
Harris H. M. 1928, 'A monographic study of the Hemipterous Family Nabidæ as it occurs in North America'. *Ent. amer.* 9, 1-98.
Heidemann O. 1911, 'Some remarks on the eggs of North American Species of Hemiptera-Heteroptera'. *Proc. ent. Soc. Wash.* 13, 128-40.
Hemming F. 1953, 'Copenhagen Decisions on Zool. Nomenclature'. *Intern. Trust Nomencl. London.*
Henneguy L. F. 1904, *Les Insectes.*
Hesse A. J. 1940, 'A New Species of *Triphleps* (Hemiptera-Heteroptera, Anthocoridæ) predaceous on the citrus thrips (*Scirtothrips aurantii* Faure) in the Transvaal'. *J. ent. Soc. S. Afr.* 3, 61-71.

Hesse A. J. 1947, 'A remarkable new dimorphic Isometopid and two other species of Hemiptera predaceous upon the red scale of Citrus'. *J. ent. Soc. S. Afr.* **10**, 31-45.

Heymons R. 1906, 'Uber einen apparat zum offnen der Eischalen bei den Pentatomiden'. *Z. wiss. InsektBiol.* **2**, 73.

Horvath G. 1894, *Feuill. jean. Nat.* **24**, 90.

Horvath G. 1911, 'Nomenclature des familles des Hémiptères'. *Ann. Mus. Nat. Hung.* **9**, 1-34.

Horvath G. 1912, 'Sur les noms des familles et des sousfamilles du règne animale'. *Verh.* **8**. *Int. Cong. Zool.* 1910.

Hungerford H. B. 1919, 'The Biology and Ecology of Aquatic and Semiaquatic Hemiptera'. *Kans. Univ. Sci. Bull.* **11**.

Hungerford H. B. 1948, 'The Corixidæ of the Western Hemisphere'. *Kans. Univ. Sci. Bull.* **32**.

Hungerford H. B. 1923, 'Notes on the Eggs of Corixidæ'. *Bull. Brooklyn ent. Soc.* **18**, 1, 14.

Imms A. D. 1934, *A General Textbook of Entomology.* (3rd ed.).

Jacobson E. 1911, 'Biological Notes on the Hemipteron *Ptilocerus ochraceus*'. *Tijdschr. Ent.* **54**, 175-9.

Jeannel R. 1919, 'Voyage de Ch. Alluaud et R Jeannel en Afrique orientale (1911-12)'. *Insectes Hémiptères,* 3.

Jeannel R. 'Les Hénicocephalides. Monographie d'un groupe d'Hémiptères Hématophages'. *Ann. Soc. ent. Fr.* **110**, 273-368.

Jordan K. H. C. 1932, 'Beitrag zur Kenntnis der Eier und Larven von Aradiden'. *Zool. Jahrb.* **63**, 3, 281-99.

Jordan L. 1922, 'Notes on the distribution of the organ of Berlese in Clinocoridæ'. *Ectoparasites* 1, 284-6.

Jourdan M. L. 1935, '*Clytiomyia helluo* F. parasite *d'Eurygaster austriaca* Schr. (Diptera-Tachinidæ)'. *Rev. franc. Ent.* **2**, 83-5.

Kalshoven L. G. E. 1950, *De Plagen van de Cultuurgewassen in Indonesie* **1**.

Kershaw J. C. W. 1909, 'On the metamorphosis and Anatomy of the Reduviid bug *Sycanus croceovittatus* Dohrn'. *Ann. Soc. ent. Belg.* **53**, 241-49.

Kershaw, J. C. W. 1910, 'On the Metamorphosis of two Coptosomine Hemiptera from Macao'. *Ann. Soc. ent. Belg.* **54**, 69-73.

Kershaw J. C. W. and Kirkaldy G. W. 1908, 'On the Metamorphosis of two Hemiptera-Heteroptera from Southern China'. *Trans. R. ent. Soc. Lond.* pt. 2, 59-62.

Kershaw J. C. W. and Kirkaldy G. W. 1909 a, 'Biological Notes on Oriental Hemiptera No. 3'. *J. Bombay nat. Hist. Soc.* Aug. 15, 333-6.

Kershaw J. C. W. and Kirkaldy G. W. 1909 b, 'Biological Notes on Oriental Hemiptera'. *J. Bombay nat. Hist. Soc.* Nov. 15, 571a-573.

Kevan D. Keith McE. 1942, 'Some observations on *Mononyx nepæformis* (Fabricius) 1775. A Toad Bug (Mononychidæ, Hemip. Heteropt.)'. *Proc. R. ent. Soc. Lond.* (A), 17, 109-10.

Kiritschenko A. N. 1913, *Insecta Hemiptera. Faune de la Russie et des pays limitrophes.* 1-395.

Kirkaldy G. W. 1899, 'A Guide to the Study of British Waterbugs'. *Entomologist* **29**, 3.

Kirkaldy G. W. 1900, 'Notes on some Sinhalese Rhynchota'. *Entomologist* **30**, 295.

Kirkaldy G. W. 1901, 'The Stridulating Organs of Waterbugs (Rhynchota) especially of Corixidæ'. *J. Quekett Micr. Cl.* **4**, 33-46.

Kirkaldy G. W. 1906, 'List of the genera of Pagiopodous Hemiptera Heteroptera'. *Trans. Amer. ent. Soc.* **32**, 47-156.

Kirkaldy G. W. 1911, 'Some Remarks on the Reduviid Subfamily Holoptilinæ and on the Species *Ptilocerus ochraceus* Montd'. *Tijdschr. Ent.* **54**, 170-4.

Kirkpatrick T. W. 1923, 'The Egyptian Cotton Seed bug (*Oxycarenus hyalini pennis* Costa)'. *Bull. Minist. Agric. Egypt* 35.

Kirkpatrick T. W. 1935-36, 'Strepsiptera attacking *Antestia*'. *Rep. E. Afr. agric. Res. St.* 8, 14-16.

Knowlton G. F. 1944, 'Pentatomidæ eaten by Utah Birds'. *J. econ. Ent.* 37, 118-19.

Knowlton G. F. and Nye W. P. 1946, 'Some Insect Food of the Sage Sparrow'. *J. Kansas ent. Soc.* 19, 4, 139.

Kormilev N. A. 1948, 'Una especia nueva de la familia Elasmodemidæ Leth. and Sev. (1896) de la República Argentina. (Hemiptera-Heteroptera, Reduvioidea)'. *Rev. Soc. ent. arg.* 14, 141-7.

Kormilev N. A. 1949, 'La Familia "Colobathristidæ" Stål en la Argentina'. *Acta zool. lilloana* Inst. Miguel Lillo, 7, 359-83.

Kullenberg B. 1944, 'Studien über die Biologie der Capsiden'. *Zool. Bidr. Uppsala.* 23.

Künckel d'Herculais L. J. 1879, 'Observations sur les Mœurs et Metamorphoses du *Gymnosoma rotundatum* L'. *Ann. Soc. ent. Fr.* (5), 9, 349-57.

Latreille P. A. 1807, *Genera Crustaceorum et Insectorum*, 1806-9.

Lent H. 1939, 'Sobre o hematofagismo de Clerada apicicornis e outros artropodos; sua importancia na trasmissao da doença de Chagas'. *Mem. Inst. Osw. Cruz.* 34.

Leston D. 1952 a, 'Notes on the Ethiopian Pentatomidæ 2. A Structure of unknown function in the Sphærocorini Stål (Hem.-Het.)'. *Entomologist* 85, 179-80.

Leston D. 1952 b, '*Oncotylus viridiflavus* Goeze (Hem. Miridæ) and its foodplant Knapweed'. *Entomologist* 85.

Leston D. 1953, 'Phlœidæ Dallas: Systematics and Morphology with Remarks on the Phylogeny of "Pentatomoidea" and upon the position of *Serbana* Distant'. *Rev. bras. Biol.* 13 (2), 121-40.

Leston D. 1954 a, 'Strigils and Stridulation in Pentatomoidea (Hem.), some new data and a review'. *Ent. mon. Mag.* Mar. 49-56.

Leston D. 1954 b, 'The Eggs of *Anthocoris gallarum-ulmi* (Deg.), (Hem. Anthocoridæ) and *Monanthia humuli* (F.) (Hem. Tingidæ) with Notes on the Eggs of Cimicoidea and Tingidoidea'. *Ent. mon. Mag.* 89, 99-102.

Leston D., Pendergrast J. G., Southwood T. R. E. 1954, 'Classification of the Terrestrial Heteroptera (Geocorisæ)'. *Nature, Lond.* 1749.

Leuckart R. 1835, 'Uber die Mikropyle und den feinern Bau der Schalenhaut bei den Insekteneiren'. *Arch. Anat. Physiol.*, Lpz. 90-264.

Mason J. W. and Maxwell-Lefroy H. 1912, 'The Food of Birds in India'. *Mem. Dep. Agric. India Ent.* 3.

Massee A. M. 1949, 'Ova of *Metatropis rufescens* H.S. (Hem. Berytidæ)'. *Ent. mon. Mag.* 85.

Maxwell-Lefroy H. 1909, *Indian Insect Life*.

Mckeown Keith C. 1934, 'The Foods of Birds from South-Western New South Wales'. *Rec. Aust. Mus.* 19, 2.

Mckeown Keith C. 1934, 'Notes on the Food of Trout and Macquarie Perch in Australia'. *Rec. Aust. Mus.* 19, 141-52.

Michalk O. 1934, 'Kannibalismus bei einen Pentatomide (Hem. Heteropt.) zugleich ein weiter Beitrag zur Technik der Nahrungsaufnahme der Wanzen'. *Ent. Z.* a.m. 48, 51-5.

Michalk O. 1935, 'Zur Morphologie und Ablage der Eier bei den Heteropteren sowie über ein System der Eiablagetypen'. *Dtsch. ent. Z.* 148-75.

Miller N. C. E. 1929 a, *Megymenum brevicorne* F. Pentatomidæ (Hem. Het.). A Minor Pest of Cucurbitaceæ and Passifloraceæ. *Malay agric. J.* 17, 12, 421-36.

Miller N. C. E. 1929 b, '*Physomerus grossipes* F. (Coreidæ, Hem. Het.). A Pest of Convolvulaceæ and Leguminosæ'. *Malay. agric. J.* 17, 11, 403-20.

Miller N. C. E. 1931 a, '*Geotomus pygmæus* Dallas (Heteroptera-Cydnidæ) attempting to suck human blood'. *Entomologist* 64, 214.

Miller N. C. E. 1931 b, 'The Bionomics of some Malayan Rhynchota (Hem. Het.)'. *Sci. Ser. Dep. Agric. S.S. and F.M.S. 5.*

Miller N. C. E. 1932 a, 'Observations on *Melamphaus faber* F. (Hem. Pyrrhocoridæ) and descriptions of early Stages'. *Bull. ent. Res.* 23, 2, 195-201.

Miller N. C. E. 1932 b, 'A Preliminary List of some Foodplants of some Malayan Insects'. *Bull. Dep. Agric. F.M.S.* 38.

Miller N. C. E. 1934, 'The Developmental Stages of Some Malayan Rhynchota'. *J. F.M.S. Mus.* 17, 3, 502-25.

Miller N. C. E. 1937, 'A New Genus of Malayan Capsidæ (Rhynchota) from Areca Palm'. *Bull. ent. Res.* 28, 4, 535-37.

Miller N. C. E. 1938 a, 'A New Subfamily of Malaysian Dysodiidæ (Rhynchota)'. *Ann. Mag. nat. Hist.* (11), 1, 498-510.

Miller N. C. E. 1938 b, 'Function of the *fossula spongiosa* or Spongy Furrow in Reduviidæ (Rhynchota)'. *Nature, Lond.* April, 23.

Miller N. C. E. 1939, 'The *fossula spongiosa* in Reduviidæ'. *Nature, Lond.* Mar. 18, 477.

Miller N. C. E. 1941, 'Insects Associated with Cocoa (*Theobroma cacao*) in Malaya'. *Bull. ent. Res.* 32, 1-15.

Miller N. C. E. 1942, 'On the Structure of the Legs in Reduviidæ (Rhynchota)'. *Proc. R. ent. Soc. Lond.* (A), 17, 49-58.

Miller N. C. E. 1953 a, 'A Note on the Ova of Urostylidæ'. *Ent. mon. Mag.* 137.

Miller N. C. E. 1953 b, 'Notes on the Biology of the Reduviidæ of Southern Rhodesia'. *Trans. zool. Soc. Lond.* 27, 541-656.

Miller N. C. E. 1953 c, 'A new Subfamily and New Genera and Species of Australian Hemiptera-Heteroptera'. *Proc. Linn. Soc. N.S.W.* 77, 233-40.

Miller N. C. E. 1955, 'The Rostrum of *Centrocnemis* Signoret 1852 (Hemiptera-Heteroptera, Reduviidæ-Reduviinæ)'. *Nature, Lond.* 175, 4458, 64.

Miller N. C. E. and Pagden H. T. 1931, 'Insect Remains in the Gut of a Cobra *Naia tripudians*'. *Nature, London.* 706.

Millikin F. B. and Wadley F. M. 1922, '*Geocoris pallens* Stål var. *decoratus* Uhl a predaceous enemy of the false cinch bug'. *Bull. Brooklyn ent. Soc.* 17, 143-6.

Mitis H. von. 1935, 'Zur biologie der Corixiden. Stridulation'. *Z. Morph. Okol. Tiere.* 30, 479-95.

Mjöberg E. 1914, 'Preliminary description of a new representative of the family Termitocoridæ'. *Tijdschr. Ent.* 35, 98-9.

Morrison J. 1932. 'Three apparently new species of Termitaphis'. *Zoologica* 3, 20, 403-8.

Muir F. 1907, 'Notes on the stridulatory organ and stink-glands of *Tessaratoma papillosa* Thunberg'. *Trans R. ent. Soc. Lond.* pt. 2.

Myers J. G. 1924, 'On the Systematic Position of the Family Termitaphidæ (Hemiptera-Heteroptera) with a description of a new genus and species from Panama'. *Psyche, Camb., Mass.* 31, 6, 259-78.

Myers J. G. 1926, 'Biological Notes on New Zealand Heteroptera'. *Trans. N.Z. Inst.* 56, 449-54.

Myers J. G. 1929, 'Facultative Blood-sucking in Phytophagous Hemiptera'. *Parasitology* 21, 472-80.

Myers J. G. 1932, 'Observations on the Family Termitaphidæ (Hemiptera-Heteroptera) with the description of a new species from Jamaica'. *Ann. Mag. nat. Hist.* (10), 9, 366-372.

Olivier, M. 1819, *Rev. sci. Bourb.* 261.

Oshanin B. 1912, *Katalog der Paläarktischen Hemiptera.*

Perez C. 1904, 'Sur les Phlœa, Hémiptères mimétiques de lichens'. *C.R. Soc. Biol., Paris* 56 (1) 429-30.

Poisson R. 1924, 'Contribution a l'étude des Hémiptères Aquatiques'. *Bull. biol.* 58.

Poisson R. 1930 a, 'Sur un Herpetomonas parasite en Normandie de *Spilostethus* (*Lygæus*) *saxatilis* (Scop.) (Hémiptères Lygæoideæ). À propos des Phytoflagelloses'. *C.R. Soc. Biol., Paris* 1057-61.

Poisson R. 1930 b, 'Herpetomonas tortum n.sp. parasite intestinal des Camptopus lateralis (Germ.) (Hemiptera, Coreidæ, Alydaria) des environs de Banyuls. Rôle possible de cet insecte comme agent transmitteur de Phytoflagellose'. C.R. Soc. Biol., Paris 1061-4.

Poisson R. 1935, 'Les Hémiptères Aquatiques (Sandaliorrhyncha) de la faune française'. Arch. Zool. exp. gén. 70, 2, 480.

Poisson R. 1951, Traité de Zoologie, Héteroptères. Tome 10, fasc, 11, 1675-1803.

Poppius B. 1909, 'Beitrage zur Kenntnis des Anthocoriden'. Acta. Soc. Sci. fenn. 37, (9).

Readio P. A. 1926, 'Studies on the Eggs of some Reduviidæ (Heteroptera)'. Kans. Univ. Sci. Bull. 16, 4, 157-79.

Readio P. A. 1927 a, 'Studies on the Biology of the Reduviidæ of America north of Mexico'. Kans. Univ. Sci. Bull. 17, 1, 5-291.

Readio P. A. 1927 b, 'Biological Notes on Phymata erosa sub sp. fasciata'. Bull. Brooklyn ent. Soc. 2, 256-62.

Reuter O. M. 1885, 'Monographia Anthocoridarum orbis terrestris'. Acta. Soc. Sci. fenn. 14, 555-758.

Reuter O. M. 1909, 'Quelques mots sur les Phyllomorphes (Hem. Coreidæ)'. Bull. Soc. ent. Fr. 264-68.

Reuter O. M. 1912, 'Bermerkungen über mein neues Heteropterensystem'. Öfvers. finska. VetenskSoc. Förh. (A), 54 (6), 1.

Reuter O. M. and Poppius B. 1909, 'Monographia Nabidarum orbis terrestris'. Acta. Soc. Sci. fenn. 37, No. 2, 1-62.

Roepke W. 1932, 'Uber Harzwanzen von Sumatra und Java'. Misc. zool. sumatra. 68.

Saunders F. 1892, The Hemiptera-Heteroptera of the British Islands.

Saunders F. 1893, Ent. mon. Mag. 99.

Schneider H. 1928, Zool. Anz. 75.

Schouteden H. 1931, Ann. Mus. Congo belge Zool. (3), 148.

Severin H. P. 1910, 'Notonecta undulata Say preying on the egg of Belostoma (Zaitha aucct) flumineum Say'. Canad. Ent. 240.

Shun-ichi-Nakao 1954, 'Biological and Ecological Studies on Agriosphodrus dohrni Signoret (Reduviidæ Hemiptera). 1, 2, Sci. Bull. Faculty Agric. Kyushu Univ. 319-36.

Silvestri F. 1911, 'Sulla posizione sistematica del genere Termitaphis Wasm. (Hemiptera) con descrizioni di due specie nuove'. Boll. Lab. Zool. Portici 5, 231-6.

Silvestri F. 1921, 'A New Species of Termitaphis (Hemiptera-Heteroptera) from India'. Rec. Indian Mus. 22, 71-4.

Slater James A. 1951, 'The Immature Stages of American Pachygronthinæ (Hemiptera-Lygæidæ)'. Iowa Acad. Sci. 58, 553-61.

Southall J. 1730, A Treatise of Bugges.

Southwood T. R. E. 1949, 'Some Notes on the Early Stages and Biology of Sehirus bicolor L. (Hem. Cydnidæ)'. Ent. mon. Mag. 85, 39-41.

Southwood T. R. E. 1953, 'Interspecific Copulation between Nabis ferus (L.) and N. rugosus (L.) (Hem. Nabidæ)'. Ent. mon. Mag. 89, 294.

Speiser P. 1904, 'Die Hemipterengattung Polyctenes Gigl. und ihre Stellung in System'. Zool. Jahrb. suppl. 7, 373-80.

Spinola M. 1837. Essai sur les Genres d'Insectes 39-40.

Spooner C. S. 1938, 'The Phylogeny of the Hemiptera based on a Study of the Head Capsule'. Univ. Ill. Bull. 35, No. 70, 1-102.

Stroyan H. L. G. 1954, 'Notes on the Early Stages of Rhopalus parumpunctatus Schill (Hemiptera-Coreidæ)'. Proc. R. ent. Soc. Lond. (A), 29, 32-8.

Takahashi R. 1921, 'Observations on the Ochteridæ'. Trans. nat. Hist. Soc. Formosa 11, 55, 119-25.

Taylor T. H. C. 1945, 'Recent Investigations of Antestia species in Uganda'. E. Afr. agric. J. 10, 4, 223-33.

Theobald F. 1895, J. S.-E. agric. Coll., Wye.

Thomas D. C. 1954, 'Notes on the Biology of some Hemiptera-Heteroptera'. *Entomologist* **87**, 25-30.

Usinger R. L. 1932, 'Miscellaneous Studies in the Heniccoephalidæ (Hemiptera)'. *Pan. Pacif. Ent.* **8**, 4, 145-56.

Usinger R. L. 1934, 'Bloodsucking among phytophagous Hemiptera'. *Canad. Ent.* 97-100.

Usinger R. L. 1939, 'Distribution and Host Relationships of *Cyrtorhinus* (Hemiptera Miridæ)'. *Proc. Harv. Ent. Soc.* 10.

Usinger R. L. 1941, 'Three New Genera of Apterous Aradidæ'. *Pan. Pacif. Ent.* **17**, 169-81.

Usinger R. L. 1942 a, 'The genus *Nysius* and its allies in the Hawaiian Islands. (Hemiptera, Lygæidæ, Orsillini)'. *Bull. Bishop Mus. Honolulu* **173**.

Usinger R. L. 1942 b, 'Revision of the Termitaphidæ (Hemiptera)'. *Pan. Pacif. Ent.* **18**.

Usinger R. L. 1943, 'A Revised Classification of the Reduvioidea with a New Subfamily from South America'. *Ann. ent. Soc. Amer.* **36**, 4, 602-18.

Usinger R. L. 1944, 'The Triatominæ of North and Central America and the West Indies and their Public Health Significance'. *Publ. Hlth. Bull. Wash.* **288**.

Usinger R. L. 1946 a, 'Insects of Guam 2. Hemiptera-Heteroptera'. *Bull. Bishop Mus. Honolulu* **189**.

Usinger R. L. 1946 b, 'Biology and Control of Ash Plant Bugs in California'. *J. econ. Ent.* **38** (5), 585-91.

Usinger R. L. 1947 a, 'Biology and Control of the Ash Lace Bug *Leptophya minor*'. *J. econ. Ent.* **39** (3), 286-9.

Usinger R. L. 1947 b, 'Native Hosts of the Mexican Chicken Bug *Hæmatosiphon inodora* (Duges) (Hemiptera Cimicidæ)'. *Pan. Pacif. Ent.* **23**, 3, 140.

Usinger R. L. 1950, 'The Origin and Distribution of Apterous Aradidæ'. *8th Int. Congr. Ent.* 1-6.

Usinger R. L. 1954, 'A New Genus of Aradidæ from the Belgian Congo with Notes on the Stridulatory Mechanisms of the Family'. *Ann. Mus. Congo belge Zool.* I Misc. Zoologica H. Schouteden, 540-3.

Verhoeff C. 1893, 'Vergleichende Untersuchungen über die Abdominal-Segments der weiblichen Hemiptera-Heteroptera) und Homoptera'. *Verh. naturh. ver. Rheinl. Westf. auch Diss Bonn.*

Villiers A. 1945, 'Un Nouvel Holoptilide (Hem.) du Sud-Ouest de l'Afrique'. *Bull. Soc. ent. Fr.* 106-7.

Villiers A. 1949, 'Revision des Emésides africains'. *Mem. Hist. nat. Paris* **23**, 2, 257-392.

Villiers A. 1952, *Hémiptères de l'Afrique noire (Punaises et Cigales) Initiations africaines.* Institut franc. d'Afrique noire, Dakar.

Walton G. A. 1936, 'Oviposition in the British Species of *Notonecta* (Hemiptera)'. *Trans. Soc. Brit. Ent.* **3**, 49-57.

Wasmann E. 1911, 'Die Ameisen und ihre Gäste'. *1st Int. Congr. Ent.* 209-34.

Waterhouse C. O. 1879, 'On the affinity of the genus *Polyctenes* Giglioli with a description of new species'. *Trans. R. ent. Soc. Lond.* 309-12.

Weber H. 1930, *Biologie der Hemipteren.*

Whitfield F. G. S. 1929, 'The Sudan Millet Bug *Agonoscelis versicolor* F.'. *Bull. ent. Res.* **20**, 209-24.

Whitfield F. G. S. 1933, 'The Bionomics and Control of *Dysdercus* (Hemiptera) in the Sudan'. *Bull. ent. Res.* **24**, 301-14.

Wigglesworth V. B. 1938, 'Climbing Organs in Insects., *Nature, Lond.* 974.

Wigglesworth V. B. 1939, *Principles of Insect Physiology.*

Wigglesworth V. B. 1954, *The Physiology of Insect Metamorphosis.*

Wigglesworth V. B. and Beament J. W. L. 1950, 'The Respiratory Mechanism of Some Insect Eggs'.| *Quart. J. micr. Sci.* **91**, 4, 429-52.

Wille J. 1929, *Monogr. PflSch.*

Wray D. L. and Brimley C. S. 1943, 'The Insect Inquilines and Victims of Pitcher Plants in N. Carolina'. *Ann. ent. Soc. Amer.* **36**, 128-37.

L

Wygodzinsky P. 1914, 'Notas sobre a biologia e o desinvolvimento do *Macrocephalus notatus* Westw. (Phymatidæ, Reduvioidea, Hemiptera)'. *Rev. Ent. Rio de J.* **15**, 139-43.

Wygodzinsky P. 1944, 'Contribucao ao Conhecimento do Genero "*Elasmodema*" Stål 1860 (Elasmodemidæ, Reduvoiodea, Hemiptera)'. *Rev. bras. Biol.* **4** (2), 193-213.

Wygodzinsky P. 1946 a, 'Sobre duas novas especies de Emesinæ do Brasil com Notas sobre "*Stenolæmoides arizonensis*" (Banks) (Reduviidæ, Hemiptera)'. *Rev. bras. Biol.* **6** (4) 509-19.

Wygodzinsky P. 1946 b, 'Contribution towards the Knowledge of the Isoderminæ (Aradidæ-Hemiptera)'. *Rev. Ent. Rio de J.* **17**, 261-73.

Wygodzinsky P. 1947 a, '*Trichotonannus setulosus* Reut. in nest of *Protermes minutus* Grassi'. *Rev. franç. Ent.* **14**, 11, 120.

Wygodzinsky P. 1947 b, 'Contribucao ao Conhecimento do Genero *Heniartes* Spinola (Apiomerinæ, Reduviidæ, Hemiptera)'. *Arch. Mus. nac., Rio de J.* **41**.

Wygodzinsky P. 1948, 'On Some Reduviidæ belonging to the Naturhistorisches Museum at Vienna (Hemiptera)'. *Rev. bras. Biol.* **8** (2), 209-24.

Wygodzinsky P. 1950, 'Schizopterinæ from Angola (Cryptostemmatidæ, Hemiptera)'. *Publ. cult. Cia. Diamant. Angola* 7, 9-47.

Yang We-I 1936, 'The Outbreak of the *Urochela distincta* Distant in Lushan'. *Bull. Fan Inst. Biol., Peking* **8**, No. 2, 57-61.

York Geo. T. 1944, 'Food Studies of *Geocoris* spp. Predators of the Beet Leafhopper'. *J. econ. Ent.* **37**, 1, 25.

INDEX

153

162   THE BIOLOGY OF THE HETEROPTERA

Stenopoda, 76, 102
Stenopodinae, 7, 86, 87
Stenoscelidea, 26
Stibaropus, 26, 43
Stiphrosomidae, 9
Strigocoris, 29
Strongylocoris leucocephalus, 110
Stethoconus cyrtopeltis, 125
Styphelia, 60
Sulpicia, 24
Syberna, 90
Sycanus, 14
Syllobus, 43

Tahitocorinae, 3, 49, 50
Tapirocoris limbatus, 92
Tectocoris lineola var. banksi, 47
Tegea, 114
— femoralis, 102
Tegeinae, 8, 114, 115
Tegellula, 114
Teratodellaria, 10
Termatophylidae, 10
Termitaphididae, 6, 71
Termitaphis, 71
Termitaradus guianae, 72
— panamensis, 71
— trinidadensis, 71
Termitocoridae, 6
Termitocoris, 71
Tessaratominae, 3, 45, 47, 48, 49, 50
Tetraripis, 130
Tetroda histeroides, 33, 46, 47
Tetyra, 28
Teuthocoris, 41
Thaumastocoridae, 5, 67
Thaumastocoris australicus, 67
Thaumastotheriinae, 5
Thea sinensis, 60
Theraptus, 55
Thodelmus, 87
Thyanta custator, 33
Thyreocorinae, 3
Tiarocoris, 41
Tiarodes cruentus, 80
— nigrirostris, 82
Tingidae, 6, 73
Tingidinae, 6
Tinginae, 6, 73
Tingis cardui, 73
Tournefortia, 60
Toxopeusiana, 103
Triatoma infestans, 37
— migrans, 36, 99
— phyllosoma, 37
— rubrofasciata, 18, 36, 99, 100
— rubrovaria, 102
Triatominae, 7, 79, 99, 100
Tribelocephala, 80, 87
Tribelocephalinae, 7, 87, 88
Trichocentrus, 68
Trichocorixa verticalis, 110

Trigona, 22
Trigonotylus brevipes, vii
Triodocoris, 41, 42
Triphleps cocciphagus, 121
— insidiosus, 121
— (Orius) persequens, 122
Tropidotylus, 42
Trypanosoma cruzi, 120
Tydides rufus, 92
Typhlocolpura, 54, 55

Urochela distincta, 52
— falloui, 52
Urolabida khasiana, 53, 58
Urolabidae, 4
Urostylidae, 4, 52
Urostylis farinaria, 52, 53, 58
— striicornis, 52
Urusa crassa, 52

Vadimon, 109
— bergrothi, 110
Valdusaria, 10
Velia africana, 130
Veliidae, 10, 130
Veliinae, 11, 131
Velitra, 98
— alboplagiata, 82, 99
— rubropicta, 35, 82, 99
Velocipedidae, 8, 115
Vernonia, 60, 117
Vesbius, 106
— purpureus, 34, 35, 120
Vescia, 96
— adamanta, 96
Vesciinae, 7, 96
Vilhennanus angolensis, 110, 128
Villanovanus dichrous, 106
Visayanocorinae, 7, 80, 85
Visayanocoris nitens, 85
Vitumnus, 108
— scenicus, 109
Voconia, 97
Volesus, 94, 95
Vulsirea variegata, 52

Xenocaucus, 88
Xenorhyncocoris, 28, 104
— caraboides, 103
— princeps, 103
Xylocorinae, 8

Yangambia, 6, 124

Zavattariocoris senegambiae, 106
Zicrona coerula, 46
Zosmenidae, 5
Zosmeridae, 5
Zelurus limbatus, 82
— luteoguttatus, 82
— spinidorsis, 102
Zygnema, 137